Grammar and Writing 4

Workbook

First Edition

Mary Hake

Christie Curtis

Hake Publishing

Grammar and Writing 4

First Edition

Workbook

Copyright ©2012 by Hake Publishing

Printed in the United States of America

ISBN: 978-1-935839-01-9

Hake Publishing
P. O. Box 662061
Arcadia, CA 91066
www.studygrammar.com

Printing History:
2 3 4 5 6 7 8 9 10   15 14 13

CPSIA Tracking and Labeling Information:
Printed by Bang Printing, Brainerd, MN, USA; Job # 131646, 07/30/13

Writing 4 Contents

Introduction		1
Lesson **1**	The Sentence	2
Lesson **2**	The Paragraph, Part 1	5
Lesson **3**	The Paragraph, Part 2	9
Lesson **4**	The Paragraph, Part 3	12
Lesson **5**	The Essay: Three Main Parts	16
Lesson **6**	The Essay: Introductory Paragraph	20
Lesson **7**	The Essay: Body Paragraphs	25
Lesson **8**	The Essay: Concluding Paragraph	31
Lesson **9**	The Essay: Transitions	36
Lesson **10**	Brainstorming for Ideas	40
Lesson **11**	Writing a Complete Essay	46
Lesson **12**	Evaluating Your Essay	47
Lesson **13**	Supporting a Topic Sentence with Experiences, Examples, Facts, and Opinions	50
Lesson **14**	Preparing to Write a Persuasive (Opinion) Essay	55
Lesson **15**	Writing the Persuasive (Opinion) Essay	58
Lesson **16**	Evaluating the Persuasive (Opinion) Essay	60
Lesson **17**	Writing a Strong Thesis Statement	63

Lesson **18**   Developing an Outline   65

Lesson **19**   Preparing to Write an Expository (Informative) Essay   68

Lesson **20**   Writing the Expository (Informative) Essay   70

Lesson **21**   Evaluating the Expository (Informative) Essay   72

Lesson **22**   Preparing to Write a Personal Narrative   75

Lesson **23**   Writing a Personal Narrative   79

Lesson **24**   Evaluating the Personal Narrative   80

Lesson **25**   Preparing to Write a Descriptive Essay   83

Lesson **26**   Writing a Descriptive Essay   89

Lesson **27**   Evaluating the Descriptive Essay   90

Lesson **28**   Writing a Chapter Summary   93

Lesson **29**   Preparing to Write an Imaginative Story   95

Lesson **30**   Writing an Imaginative Story   99

Lesson **31**   Evaluating the Imaginative Story   100

Lesson **32**   Writing about Literature   103

Lesson **33**   Writing about an Informational Text   105

Lesson **34**   Preparing to Write a Research Paper: The Working Bibliography   107

Lesson **35**   Preparing to Write a Research Paper: Notes, Thesis, Outline   111

Lesson **36**   Writing the Research Paper   113

Lesson **37**   Evaluating the Research Paper   116

Lesson **38**   Idioms and Proverbs   119

Appendix   Example Answers for Lessons 18, 25, 32, 33, 38   121

Introduction

People can share their thoughts, ideas, and feelings with others by signing, speaking, singing, drawing pictures, taking photographs, making faces, or writing. You might think of other ways as well, but one of the most common ways for people to communicate is through writing.

You have much to communicate. No two people are exactly alike. There is not another *you* on earth. Your thoughts and experiences are not exactly the same as anyone else's, so you have unique ideas to share with others. Writing is a good way to do that, for it allows you to record your ideas and memories and save them for the future, maybe even for future generations.

Good writing is a skill; it takes practice just as any other skill does. A masterful musician practices every day, and so does an excellent basketball player. In *Grammar and Writing 4*, you will practice recording your thoughts and ideas on paper to improve your skill.

Writing journal entries will give you daily practice. In addition, the following writing lessons will help you to develop good sentences, strong paragraphs, and well-organized, cohesive essays. You will learn to write clearly and effectively, which is an important lifetime skill.

One of the most important tools you as a writer will need is a **small notebook or card file** for collecting ideas, for jotting down questions or things that you notice, for saving your memories and dreams, and for writing down favorite words, names, and catchy phrases from things you read or hear. You might even keep drawings, photos, or newspaper clippings in your notebook. This is a place to keep bits and pieces that you might someday use in a poem, essay, or story. You will carry this small notebook or card file with you *everywhere* and make notes in it often.

In addition to your small notebook or card file, you will need a **three-ring binder** for keeping your daily journals and your writing assignments from this packet. Your three-ring binder will help you to organize your work so that you can easily refer back to earlier assignments when necessary.

LESSON 1

The Sentence

The Sentence We have learned that a **sentence** expresses a complete thought. Good sentences are the building blocks of effective writing. A good sentence can be long or short. A long sentence is not necessarily better than a short one.

Our writing goal is not to fill up a page with many words. Instead, our goal is to write clearly so that a reader says, "Aha, I see. I understand what you wrote." Too many words can confuse or bore a reader. A skillful writer makes every word count.

In this lesson, we shall practice writing sentences in which every word adds important information without being repetitive. We can do this two different ways: (1) by combining two or more sentences into one compact sentence and (2) by writing a wordy sentence another way.

Combining Sentences Sometimes, combining the information from two or more sentences can reduce the number of unnecessary words in our writing. Consider the sentences below.

WORDY: Ray has black hair. Ray has brown eyes.

BETTER: Ray has black hair and brown eyes.

WORDY: Ray is my uncle. Ray plays softball.

BETTER: My Uncle Ray plays softball.

WORDY: Ray surfed. Marie surfed. I did too.

BETTER: Ray, Marie, and I surfed.

WORDY: Rex likes balls. He likes birds. He also likes cats.

BETTER: Rex likes balls, birds, and cats.

Example 1 Combine information from the two sentences below to make one sentence.

Ray fixes cars. Ray fixes bicycles.

Instead of repeating "Ray fixes," we put all the information into one compact sentence:

Ray fixes cars and bicycles.

Example 2   Combine information from the two sentences below to make one sentence.

> My parakeet is green. My parakeet lives in a cage.

Instead of repeating "My parakeet," we put all the information into one compact sentence:

> **My green parakeet lives in a cage.**

Writing it another way   Sometimes, there is a shorter, more direct way to write a sentence. Consider the following sentence:

> The salad was made by Elena.

In the sentence above, Elena does the action. She makes the salad. Yet, Elena is not the subject of the sentence. We find her at the end of the sentence. Instead, "salad" is the subject, but "salad" does not act. It is only acted upon; it is made by someone. We call this passive voice.

Whenever possible, it is better to write a sentence in which the subject does the action (active voice), as in the sentence below:

> Elena made the salad.

Compare the sentence pairs below.

WORDY: A tree was climbed by a bear.
BETTER: A bear climbed a tree.

WORDY: The ball was caught by Rex.
BETTER: Rex caught the ball.

WORDY: They are taught by Miss Ng.
BETTER: Miss Ng teaches them.

WORDY: He was surprised by the happy ending.
BETTER: The happy ending surprised him.

Example 3   Rewrite the sentence below in a shorter, more direct way. Use the active voice.

> The field was plowed by Manny.

If we turn the sentence around, putting the last part first, we can make a more compact sentence in which the subject does the action:

Manny plowed the field.

Example 4 Rewrite the sentence below in a shorter, more direct way. Use the active voice.

Ian is admired by his buddies.

If we turn the sentence around, putting the last part first, we can make a more compact and direct sentence:

Ian's buddies admire him.

Practice For a–c, combine sentences to make one compact sentence.

a. Tina is my friend. Tina has a bulldog.

_____

b. Flo buys shoes. Flo buys socks. Flo buys pants.

_____

c. The car is new. The car should run well.

_____

For d–f, rewrite the sentence in a shorter, more direct way. Use the active voice. (Hint: Put the last part of the sentence first.)

d. The band was directed by the conductor.

_____

e. Ward was startled by a loud boom.

_____

f. A loud boom was made by thunder.

_____

LESSON 2

The Paragraph, Part 1

The Paragraph   A **paragraph** is a group of sentences that builds on a main idea or topic. A good paragraph presents one main idea and develops it with additional sentences giving more specific information about that main idea.

The Topic Sentence   The **topic sentence** is a complete sentence telling the main idea of a paragraph. Often, the topic sentence is the first sentence of a paragraph, but not always. Topic sentences are underlined in the paragraphs below:

> <u>Spines protect a hedgehog.</u> A hedgehog has spines everywhere on its body except its face, legs, and belly. Whenever an enemy comes near, the hedgehog rolls up into a tight little ball. Enemies avoid that prickly ball.

> Sloths are sleepy tree-dwellers. They sleep up to twenty hours per day. They are so sluggish that algae grow on their fur. Sloths live in tropical rainforests. They look like monkeys but are related to armadillos and anteaters. <u>Sloths are interesting animals</u>.

Example 1   Underline the topic sentence in the following paragraph:

> There are two main types of sloths. Two-clawed sloths are slightly bigger and spend more time hanging upside down than the three-clawed sloths. The coloring on the faces of the three-toed sloths makes them look like they are always smiling.

The paragraph above is all about the two main types of sloths. Therefore, we underline the topic sentence as follows:

> <u>**There are two main types of sloths.**</u> Two-clawed sloths are slightly bigger and spend more time hanging upside down than the three-clawed sloths. The coloring on the faces of the three-toed sloths makes them look like they are always smiling.

Example 2   The paragraph below contains a sentence that does not support the topic sentence. Read the paragraph carefully. Then, draw a line through the sentence that does not belong.

At one time, American alligators were on the list of endangered animals. These alligators have since been removed from the list. There are now over one million living American alligators. Amelia saw a crocodile yesterday. American alligators live in Louisiana and Florida.

We see that the paragraph above is all about American alligators. That Amelia saw a crocodile has nothing to do with the American alligator topic, so we cross out the sentence as follows:

At one time, American alligators were on the list of endangered animals. These alligators have since been removed from the list. There are now over one million living American alligators. ~~Amelia saw a crocodile yesterday.~~ American alligators live in Louisiana and Florida.

Practice and Review   For paragraphs a–c, underline the topic sentence.

a.   With ears nearly six inches long, the fennec fox weighs only about two pounds when full grown. This little fox, as small as a rabbit, lives in deserts of North Africa, the Sinai Peninsula, and the Arabian Peninsula. The fennec fox is the smallest fox in the world.

b.   Ned painted a picture of an American bison. Also called a buffalo, the mammal Ned painted was massive. He used much brown and black paint on the beast's shaggy fur and two curved horns. Beneath it, Ned wrote, "Symbol of the Old West."

c.   The American bullfrog lives in freshwater ponds, lakes, and marshes. Amphibians are a group of animals that includes frogs, toads, and salamanders. Amphibians spend their entire lives near or in water. The American bullfrog is one type of amphibian.

For paragraphs d–f, draw a line through the sentence that does not belong.

d.   The largest snake in the world is the green anaconda. It can grow up to thirty feet in length, and it can weigh up to 550 pounds. The green anaconda belongs to a family of snakes called constrictors. ~~Have you seen a rattlesnake?~~ Constrictors kill their prey by squeezing it until it stops breathing.

e.   The green anaconda is an aquatic snake. It lives in swamps, marshes, and slow-moving rivers. The green anaconda is a nocturnal reptile. This means that the snake is most active at night. ~~Jenan visited the zoo.~~ The green anaconda can move on land, but it prefers water because it is easier for the big snake to move its body.

f.   One interesting dinosaur is *Ankylosaurus magniventris*. The Ankylosaurus's body was covered with hard, bony plates to protect it from its most feared enemy: *T-rex*. Its head had two horns, and rows of spikes lined its body. ~~The green anaconda swallows its prey whole.~~ Only by flipping the Ankylosaurus over could an enemy find its weak spot.

For g–i, combine sentences to make one compact sentence.

g. The sun was warm. The sun dried our wet boots.

_____

h. Ned paints bison. Ned paints dinosaurs.

_____

i. Chad is my cousin. Chad collects coins.

_____

For j and k, rewrite the sentence in a shorter, more direct way. Use the active voice. (Hint: Put the last part of the sentence first.)

j. Rudy was frightened by the anaconda.

_____

k. Shelby's jokes are enjoyed by most people.

_____

LESSON 3

The Paragraph, Part 2

Logical Order   We have learned that a paragraph is a group of sentences that builds on a main idea, or topic. A good paragraph presents one main idea and develops it with additional sentences giving more specific information about that main idea. The supporting sentences are arranged in a **logical order.** The paragraph below tells what happened first, next, and last.

> Jessie wanted to plant a vegetable garden. First, she turned over the soil and watered it, removing all the weeds. Next, she chose her seeds and decided where to plant each kind. Then, she sowed the seeds, covering them lightly with soil. Now, she is waiting for her vegetable seeds to sprout.

Sometimes, creating a logical order means placing sentences in order of importance, usually ending with the most important point, as in the paragraph below.

> Jessie's ability to grow her own food is very helpful. It saves her family a great deal of money. More importantly, it allows Jessie's family to eat fresh, nutritious vegetables. Most important of all, growing her own vegetables gives Jessie a sense of accomplishment.

Example   Arrange the sentences below in a logical order to create a good paragraph.

- Finally, tadpoles change to frogs with the ability to live on land.

- Then, they continue life as tadpoles in the water.

- Because frogs are amphibians, they develop in a different way from other animals.

- First, their eggs hatch.

What happened first? Then what happened? We can number the sentences like this:

4 Finally, tadpoles change to frogs with the ability to live on land.

3 Then, they continue life as tadpoles in the water.

1 Because frogs are amphibians, they develop in a different way from other animals.

2 First, their eggs hatch.

Now, we can arrange these sentences in order to make the following paragraph:

> Because frogs are amphibians, they develop in a different way from other animals. First, their eggs hatch. Then, they continue life as tadpoles in the water. Finally, tadpoles change to frogs with the ability to live on land.

Practice and Review

a. Read the sentences below. Then, number the sentences according to what happens first, next, etc. (Place numbers one through four in the boxes.)

☐ Then, she begins to color.

☐ Finally, she shows her friend the pretty picture.

☐ Elle wants to be creative, so she decides to do art.

☐ First, she finds crayons and paper.

b. Finish writing the paragraph below, adding three or more sentences in a logical order.

> After school, I shall do something creative.

First_____

_____

_____

_____

_____

_____

_____

_____

c. Underline the topic sentence in the paragraph below.

After growing up in the United States, Thomas married and moved to Germany. While there, he traveled to Austria, Belgium, France, Italy, the Czech Republic, and Norway. Next year, he plans to visit China and India. Thomas is a world traveler.

d. Draw a line through the sentence that does not belong in the paragraph below.

After Thomas left Germany, he lived in the United States once again. However, he and his wife decided to make England their new home. Jenny went to Australia. While in England, Thomas visited Spain, Ireland, and Scotland.

For e and f, combine sentences to make one compact sentence.

e. Darla has brown eyes. Darla has long eyelashes.

_____

f. Rex digs holes. Rex jumps fences.

_____

For g and h, rewrite the sentence in a shorter, more direct way. Use the active voice. (Hint: Put the last part of the sentence first.)

g. Neighbors were bothered by Rex's barking.

_____

h. The Bactrian camel was studied by Ed.

_____

LESSON
4

The Paragraph, Part 3

We have learned that a paragraph is a group of sentences building on a main idea or topic. A good paragraph presents one main idea and develops it with additional sentences that give more information about that main idea. In this lesson, we shall learn one way to produce sentences that support a topic sentence.

Supporting Sentences

You can write sentences that support a topic sentence by asking yourself *who, what, when, where, why,* and *how* questions. Suppose that you wanted to write a paragraph using the topic sentence below.

Summer is an enjoyable time of the year.

You can ask yourself the following questions:

Who enjoys summer?

What do people enjoy about summer?

When do people enjoy summer?

Where do people have fun during summer?

Why is summer enjoyable?

How can people enjoy summer?

Answering the questions above will help you to think of supporting sentences for your topic sentence. You might write a paragraph like this:

Summer is an enjoyable time of the year. Some people really like warm weather. Others enjoy summer sports, such as swimming, boating, and hiking. During June, July, and August, people often take time away from work and school to travel, to stay up later at night, and to sleep later in the morning. Students like the fact that they have no homework!

Example Consider this topic sentence:

We can improve our eating habits.

Write some *who, what, when, where, why* and *how* questions to get ideas for supporting sentences. Then, write a paragraph.

We can ask the following questions:

Who can improve their eating habits?

What can we do to improve our eating habits?

When can we improve our eating habits?

Where can we go to improve our eating habits?

Why do our eating habits need improving?

How can we improve our eating habits?

Answering the questions above helps us to write the following paragraph:

> People can improve their eating habits. Some people already eat well, but they still can improve. Everyone can improve. Learning as much as possible about the human body and its requirements is a good place to begin. No matter what the person's age, it is never too late to begin eating more nutritiously.

Practice and Review

a. Read the sentences below. Then, number them according to what happens first, next, etc. (Place numbers one through five in the boxes.)

☐ Next, she jumps out of bed.

☐ Finally, she grabs her backpack, jacket, and lunch and runs out the door.

☐ Jade awakens to the sound of her alarm clock ringing, a reminder that it is time to get up.

☐ She puts on her white blouse, plaid skirt, shoes, and socks.

☐ First, she reaches over and turns off the alarm.

b. On the lines below, complete *who, what, when, where, why,* and *how* questions for this topic sentence: There are many things that I like about my school.

*Who*_____?

What _____?

When _____?

Where _____?

Why _____?

How _____?

Now, in your mind, answer the questions above to help you finish writing the paragraph below.

There are many things that I like about my school.

_____

_____

_____

_____

_____

_____

_____

_____

_____

_____

c. Underline the topic sentence in the paragraph below.

Athena has attended many different schools. Five years ago, she went to kindergarten at a school in Texas. Last year, she started third grade at a school in Louisiana. This year, Athena is in a fourth grade class in Florida. She wonders where she will go to school next year.

d. Draw a line through the sentence that does not belong in the paragraph below.

Cory planned ahead for his surfing trip. He made a list of the items that he needed for the adventure. First, he found a bag to hold all of his gear. Then, he packed a swimsuit, towel, bottle of water, and bar of wax. Cory owned a skateboard. After checking over his list, he grabbed his bag and headed out the door.

For e and f, combine sentences to make one compact sentence.

e. Cory has a swimsuit. Cory has a towel.

_____

f. Mr. Hong teaches math. Mr. Hong teaches reading. Mr. Hong teaches writing.

_____

For g and h, rewrite the sentence in a shorter, more direct way. Use active voice. (Hint: Put the last part of the sentence first.)

g. I was alarmed by the news.

_____

h. The garden was planted by Jessie.

_____

Additional Practice Write a paragraph using one of the following sentences as your topic sentence, or make up your own topic sentence. Add at least three sentences to support or more fully explain your topic sentence. (Think: Who? What? When? Where? Why? How?)

1. Being a good friend requires certain skills.

2. There are many things I can do to help others.

3. Daily exercise is important.

4. I have fun with my family.

LESSON 5

The Essay: Three Main Parts

We have learned that a paragraph is a group of sentences that builds on a main idea, or topic.

The Essay An **essay** is a group of paragraphs that builds on one main idea. In this lesson, we shall learn about the structure of an essay.

An essay has three main parts:

1. Introductory Paragraph

2. Body or Support Paragraphs

3. Concluding Paragraph

Below is a chart that shows the structure of the typical five-paragraph essay. Each box represents one paragraph.

```
┌─────────────────────────────────────┐
│ Introductory Paragraph              │
│                                     │
│                                     │
└─────────────────────────────────────┘


┌─────────────────────────────────────┐
│ Body Paragraph                      │
│                                     │
│                                     │
└─────────────────────────────────────┘
┌─────────────────────────────────────┐
│ Body Paragraph                      │
│                                     │
│                                     │
└─────────────────────────────────────┘
┌─────────────────────────────────────┐
│ Body Paragraph                      │
│                                     │
│                                     │
└─────────────────────────────────────┘


┌─────────────────────────────────────┐
│ Concluding Paragraph                │
│                                     │
│                                     │
└─────────────────────────────────────┘
```

Example   From memory, reproduce the chart that shows the structure of a typical five-paragraph essay.

We can reproduce the chart like this:

Introductory Paragraph

Body Paragraph

Body Paragraph

Body Paragraph

Concluding Paragraph

Practice and Review   **a.** Read the sentences below. Then, number them according to what happens first, next, etc. (Place numbers one through four in the boxes.)

1	Sergio must do his chores before school.
4	Finally, Sergio is ready for school.
3	Then, he empties the trash cans.
2	First, he makes his bed.

b. In your mind, answer some *who, what, when, where, why,* and *how* questions about this topic sentence: I would like to learn some new skills. Then, write three or more supporting sentences to complete the paragraph.

I would like to learn some new skills. *Being better in math I want to achieve. To acomplish this, I will use flashcards at home and at school for practice. Starting with one and moving to twelves is the process I will use. My parents can time me as well. I will attain math skills through hard work.*

c. Underline the topic sentence in the paragraph below.

<u>Abraham Lincoln was one of the Nation's greatest leaders.</u> His genius was to surround himself with people who could argue with him and question his motives. He learned from his mistakes, and he took responsibility for the mistakes of others.

d. Draw a line through the sentence that does not belong in the paragraph below.

Some historians believe that Lincoln's superb leadership came from his ability to admit his errors and learn from his mistakes. Lincoln put his past hurts behind him, and he did not hold grudges. ~~George McClellan was head of the Union Army for a time.~~ Lincoln's greatest flaw was his desire to give people a second or even a third chance.

For e and f, combine sentences to make one compact sentence.

e. Carlos owns a shiny bicycle. It is red.

Carlos owns a shiny, red bicycle.

f. Miss Ng has taught in South Dakota. She has taught in Oregon. She has taught in New York.

Miss Ng has taught in South, Oregon, and New York.

For g and h, rewrite the sentence in a shorter, more direct way. Use active voice. (Hint: Put the last part of the sentence first.)

g. The horse might have been startled by the thunder.

The thunder might have startled the horse.

h. That waltz was composed by Brahms.

Brams composed that waltz.

i. From memory, reproduce the chart showing the structure of a typical five-paragraph essay.

Induction Paragraph

Body Paragraph

Body Paragraph

Body Paragraph

Concluding Paragraph

LESSON 6

The Essay: Introductory Paragraph

We have learned that an essay has three main parts: (1) the introductory paragraph, (2) the body paragraphs, and (3) the concluding paragraph. In this lesson, we shall learn what makes up the introductory paragraph.

Introductory Paragraph

The **introductory paragraph** is the first paragraph of an essay. It introduces the main subject of the essay. The introductory paragraph has two parts:

1. An Introductory Sentence grabs the reader's interest.

2. A Thesis Statement tells the subject of the essay.

We can now add more detail to our chart showing the structure of an essay:

```
┌─────────────────────────────────────┐
│ Introductory Paragraph              │
│     1. Introductory Sentence        │
│     2. Thesis Statement             │
└─────────────────────────────────────┘


┌─────────────────────────────────────┐
│ Body Paragraph                      │
│                                     │
│                                     │
└─────────────────────────────────────┘

┌─────────────────────────────────────┐
│ Body Paragraph                      │
│                                     │
│                                     │
└─────────────────────────────────────┘

┌─────────────────────────────────────┐
│ Body Paragraph                      │
│                                     │
│                                     │
└─────────────────────────────────────┘


┌─────────────────────────────────────┐
│ Concluding Paragraph                │
│                                     │
│                                     │
└─────────────────────────────────────┘
```

The thesis statement is underlined in the introductory paragraph below.

> Many animals have interesting characteristics, but camels are one of the most peculiar in appearance. <u>Camels are fascinating for three reasons.</u>

In the introductory paragraph above, the first sentence (sometimes called the "hook") grabs the reader's attention so that he or she will keep reading. The second sentence, the thesis statement, clearly tells the subject of the essay: three reasons why camels are fascinating.

The reader expects to find these three reasons in the body of the essay. Perhaps, each of the three body paragraphs will give one reason.

Example 1 Underline the thesis statement in the following introductory paragraph.

> People are often looking for paradise, and Tamika has found it! The ideal place on a summer afternoon is her local park, for there she can relax, swim, and play.

We see that this essay will be about an ideal place, which is the local park. So, we underline the second sentence.

> People are often looking for paradise, and Tamika has found it! <u>The ideal place on a summer afternoon is her local park, for there she can relax, swim, and play.</u>

Example 2 Complete the chart that shows the structure of an essay. Include what you have learned from this lesson about the introductory paragraph.

We reproduce the chart that shows the two parts of the introductory paragraph: (1) the introductory sentence and (2) the thesis statement.

```
┌─────────────────────────────────┐
│  Introductory Paragraph          │
│     1. Introductory sentence     │
│     2. Thesis statement          │
└─────────────────────────────────┘

┌─────────────────────────────────┐
│  Body Paragraph                  │
│                                  │
│                                  │
└─────────────────────────────────┘

┌─────────────────────────────────┐
│  Body Paragraph                  │
│                                  │
│                                  │
└─────────────────────────────────┘

┌─────────────────────────────────┐
│  Body Paragraph                  │
│                                  │
│                                  │
└─────────────────────────────────┘

┌─────────────────────────────────┐
│  Concluding Paragraph            │
│                                  │
│                                  │
└─────────────────────────────────┘
```

Practice and Review

a. Underline the thesis statement in the introductory paragraph below.

Almost everybody likes fresh berries. There are many varieties of berries to please most everyone's taste buds. <u>Three of the most popular berries are strawberries, raspberries, and blueberries.</u>

b. Read the sentences below. Then, number them in order of importance (ending with the most important) by placing numbers two through four in the boxes.

[1] Ray exercises every day for three reasons.

[3] Moreover, exercise keeps his muscles strong and flexible.

[4] Most important of all, he knows that exercise keeps his heart strong and healthy.

[2] First, he enjoys exercising, for he feels refreshed afterward.

c. In your mind, think of *who, what, when, where, why,* and *how* questions for this topic sentence: I can do some things to help other people. Use the answers to your questions to help you write supporting sentences to complete the paragraph.

I can do some things to help other people. I can help my mom. I can help her by making dinner. I can help her after homework. I can help her in the kitchen. I could help because it's the right thing to do. I could gather the ingredients.

d. Underline the topic sentence in the paragraph below.

In fifth grade, I shall be walking to school rather than riding the bus. Also, I shall be buying my lunch instead of bringing a sack lunch. Once I am settled in the routine of the classroom, I shall have more homework than I had in the fourth grade. Fifth grade will bring me many new responsibilities.

e. Draw a line through the sentence that does not belong in the paragraph below.

Jan wants to improve as a volleyball player. With instruction from her coach, she places her feet in a ready stance. She extends her arms in front of her in anticipation of an oncoming ball. Jan has new shoes. When she sees a volleyball coming her way, she puts her hands together and gently passes the ball to the setter. By repeating these actions over and over, Jan will become a better player.

24

For f and g, combine sentences to make one compact sentence.

f.   The great white shark is long at birth. It is five feet.

The great white shark is long at birth it it five feet.

g.   Roy is my classmate. Roy plays the piano and the guitar.

Roy is my classmate he plays the piano and the guitar.

h.   Rewrite the sentence below in a shorter, more direct way. Hint: Put the last part of the sentence first.

That soup was made by Aunt Mary.

Aunt Mary made that soup.

i.   From memory, complete the chart that shows the structure of a typical five-paragraph essay.

_____ Paragraph
1. _____
2. _____

_____ Paragraph

_____ Paragraph

_____ Paragraph

_____ Paragraph

25

LESSON 7

The Essay: Body Paragraphs

We have learned that the introductory paragraph, the first paragraph of an essay, grabs the reader's interest and gives the subject of the essay. In this lesson, we shall learn about the body paragraphs of an essay.

Body Paragraphs The **body paragraphs,** or support paragraphs, follow the introductory paragraph and precede the concluding paragraph. Body paragraphs prove or explain the thesis statement. They provide examples, facts, opinions, or arguments to help the reader understand that the thesis statement is true.

Topic Sentence Each body paragraph has a **topic sentence** that tells the content of the paragraph. The topic sentence is followed by supporting sentences.

Supporting Sentences **Supporting sentences** support, prove, or explain the topic sentence of that body paragraph. At least three supporting sentences are usually needed to make a strong paragraph.

Each body paragraph looks like this:

> Topic Sentence
>
> 1. Supporting sentence
>
> 2. Supporting sentence
>
> 3. Supporting sentence

Now, we can add more detail to our chart showing the structure of an essay. To each Body Paragraph box, we can add the topic sentence and three or more supporting sentences.

Example 1 Reproduce the chart that shows the structure of an essay. Add the information from this lesson about body paragraphs.

26

We reproduce the chart below, adding the topic sentence and three or more supporting sentences to each Body Paragraph.

```
┌─────────────────────────────────────────┐
│ Introductory Paragraph                   │
│      1. Introductory sentence            │
│      2. Thesis statement                 │
└─────────────────────────────────────────┘

┌─────────────────────────────────────────┐
│ Body Paragraph                           │
│   • Topic sentence                       │
│      1. Supporting sentence              │
│      2. Supporting sentence              │
│      3. Supporting sentence              │
├─────────────────────────────────────────┤
│ Body Paragraph                           │
│   • Topic sentence                       │
│      1. Supporting sentence              │
│      2. Supporting sentence              │
│      3. Supporting sentence              │
├─────────────────────────────────────────┤
│ Body Paragraph                           │
│   • Topic sentence                       │
│      1. Supporting sentence              │
│      2. Supporting sentence              │
│      3. Supporting sentence              │
└─────────────────────────────────────────┘

┌─────────────────────────────────────────┐
│ Concluding Paragraph                     │
│                                          │
│                                          │
└─────────────────────────────────────────┘
```

Example 2 Using the introductory paragraph below, write a topic sentence for each body paragraph to further develop the thesis statement of the essay.

People are often looking for paradise, and Tamika has found it! <u>The ideal place on a summer afternoon is her local park, for there she can relax, swim, and play.</u>

We can write the following three topic sentences to further explain our thesis statement.

Topic sentence #1: Tamika finds the shady park relaxing.

Topic sentence #2: She loves to swim in the lake.

Topic sentence #3: The local park is a great place for playing many different games.

27

Each of these topic sentences can be developed into a body paragraph by adding supporting sentences to further explain the topic sentence. For example, we might develop the first body paragraph like this:

topic sentence → *Tamika finds the shady park relaxing.* It is a quiet place with tall trees. She likes to lie on the grass face up, watching billowy clouds float by and listening to bird songs. No one bothers her there. She can forget all her worries in that restful place.

{ supporting sentences

In the body paragraph above, supporting sentences follow the topic sentence to explain why the shady park is relaxing.

Practice and Review **a.** Write three topic sentences to support the thesis statement in the following introductory paragraph:

There are many amazing people in the world, but none are as amazing as my friend. <u>My friend should be honored for three reasons.</u>

Hint: Think about an amazing friend of yours. What makes that friend amazing? Is he or she generous? Helpful? Kind? Hard-working? Skillful at something? Knowledgeable? You might also think, *Who? What? When? Where? Why?*

Topic sentence #1: My friend Alinn is should be honored because she is kind to me.

Topic sentence #2: She is also very helpful at her house she cleans stuff up.

Topic sentence #3: She is very knowledgeable by trying to get A's on everything.

(practice continued on next page)

b. Now, develop one of your topic sentences from Practice *a* into a body paragraph. Add at least three supporting sentences.

_____

_____

_____

_____

_____

_____

_____

_____

_____

_____

c. Underline the thesis statement in the introductory paragraph below.

   Many people shudder at the thought of great white sharks, but I find them interesting. I like to study their eating habits, their size, and their appearance.

d. Read the sentences below. Then, number them according to what happens first, next, etc. (Place numbers one through four in the boxes.)

☐ Once the great white shark sees its next meal, it swims underneath it.

☐ The great white shark hunts the oceans for seals or sea lions.

☐ Finally, the great white shark swallows its prey whole.

☐ Then, the shark swims upward with a burst of speed, breaching with the prey in its mouth.

e. Underline the topic sentence in the paragraph below.

Sand tiger sharks are another type of shark. Like other shark species, they breathe underwater through gills. However, sand tiger sharks are the only sharks that come to the surface of the water and gulp air. This is to make them buoyant. Sand tiger sharks float motionless in the water, waiting for their prey.

f. Draw a line through the sentence that does not belong in the paragraph below.

Sand tiger sharks prefer to hunt at night. They float in shallow water just above the ocean floor. This habit is the reason for the "sand" in their name. The hammerhead shark looks strange. The "tiger" comes from the sand tiger sharks' huge appetite.

For g and h, combine sentences to make one compact sentence.

g. Nate caught two fish. The fish were big and white.

_____

h. Josh is my buddy. Josh plays the banjo.

_____

i. Rewrite the sentence below in a shorter, more direct way. Use the active voice. Hint: Put the last part of the sentence first.

The berries were picked by Nan and Ed.

_____

(practice continued on next page)

j. From memory, complete the chart that shows the structure of a typical five-paragraph essay.

```
┌─────────────────────────────────────┐
│ _____ Paragraph          │
│    1. _____              │
│    2. _____              │
└─────────────────────────────────────┘

┌─────────────────────────────────────┐
│ _____ Paragraph          │
│    _____ sentence        │
│    1. _____ sentence     │
│    2. _____ sentence     │
│    3. _____ sentence     │
└─────────────────────────────────────┘

┌─────────────────────────────────────┐
│ _____ Paragraph          │
│    _____ sentence        │
│    1. _____ sentence     │
│    2. _____ sentence     │
│    3. _____ sentence     │
└─────────────────────────────────────┘

┌─────────────────────────────────────┐
│ _____ Paragraph          │
│    _____ sentence        │
│    1. _____ sentence     │
│    2. _____ sentence     │
│    3. _____ sentence     │
└─────────────────────────────────────┘

┌─────────────────────────────────────┐
│ _____ Paragraph          │
│                                     │
│                                     │
└─────────────────────────────────────┘
```

31

LESSON 8

The Essay: Concluding Paragraph

We have learned about the first two main parts of an essay: the introduction and the body. In this lesson, we shall learn about the third and final main part of an essay: the conclusion.

Concluding Paragraph

The **concluding paragraph** is the final paragraph of an essay. It summarizes the ideas expressed in the body of the essay. The concluding paragraph has three important parts:

1. A restatement of the thesis statement

2. A reference to each topic sentence

3. A clincher sentence (last one)

Your "last words" will leave a lasting impression on your readers.

Notice how the concluding paragraph below refers to the three topic sentences in Example 2 of Lesson 7.

Topic sentence #1: Tamika finds the shady park <u>relax</u>ing.

Topic sentence #2: She loves to <u>swim</u> in the lake.

Topic sentence #3: The local park is a great place for <u>play</u>ing many different games.

CONCLUDING PARAGRAPH:

Restatement of thesis → In conclusion, for Tamika there is no better place than her local park. There, she can (relax), (swim), and
Reference to each topic sentence → (play) games. Tamika would rather be there than anyplace else in the world! ← Clincher (last sentence)

We see that the concluding paragraph above restates the thesis and contains a reference to each topic sentence. It summarizes the main ideas in the essay and ends with a strong statement. The last words will leave a lasting impression on the reader.

32

Example 1   Write a concluding paragraph for an essay with the following thesis statement and topic sentences:

> Thesis statement: Many people fear great white sharks, but I find them interesting.

> Topic sentence #1: Great white sharks have unique eating habits.

> Topic sentence #2: The size of these sharks is incredible.

> Topic sentence #3: Even the appearance of this shark is unusual.

Based on the thesis statement and topic sentences above, we can write a concluding paragraph like this:

> **In conclusion, great white sharks are interesting sea creatures. They have unique eating habits, incredible size, and unusual appearance. Great white sharks are truly a peculiar fish!**

Example 2   On the next page, complete the chart showing the structure of an essay. Include the three important parts of a concluding paragraph.

33

We reproduce the chart below, adding the two important parts of the concluding paragraph.

Introductory Paragraph
1. Introductory sentence
2. Thesis statement

Body Paragraph
• Topic sentence
1. Supporting sentence
2. Supporting sentence
3. Supporting sentence

Body Paragraph
• Topic sentence
1. Supporting sentence
2. Supporting sentence
3. Supporting sentence

Body Paragraph
• Topic sentence
1. Supporting sentence
2. Supporting sentence
3. Supporting sentence

Concluding Paragraph
1. Restatement of thesis
2. Reference to each topic sentence
3. Clincher sentence

Practice and Review

a. Write a concluding paragraph based on the thesis statement "My friend should be honored for three reasons" and the three topic sentences that you wrote for Lesson 7.

_____

_____

_____

_____

_____

_____

b. Underline the thesis statement in the introductory paragraph below.

> Reading books provides people with adventures and information that they would not normally receive. There are many types of books from which to choose. I enjoy reading mystery, science fiction, and humorous stories.

c. Read the sentences below. Then, number them according to what happens first, next, etc. (Place numbers one through four in the boxes.)

☐ He clears the dishes from the dinner table.

☐ Horatio's father thanks his son for his help.

☐ Horatio wants to help his father clean up after dinner.

☐ Then, he washes the dishes and puts them away.

d. Underline the topic sentence in the paragraph below.

> Ellen cannot sleep. The neighbor's dog will not stop barking. A cat is yowling near her window. The clock in Ellen's room is ticking too loudly, and a bright light in the hallway is bothering her eyes. Also, Ellen is worrying about tomorrow's grammar test. Poor Ellen! She will be tired in the morning.

e. Draw a line through the sentence that does not belong in the paragraph below.

> There are more than 360 species of sharks. Sharks belong to a group of fishes that also includes rays and skates. Their bodies are held together by cartilage rather than by bones. Amphibians begin their lives in the water. The tip of a human's nose is made of cartilage like that found in a shark. A group of sharks is called a shoal or school.

For f and g, combine sentences to make one compact sentence.

f. Kate plays baseball. Kate plays basketball.

g. Mercy has a new bicycle. It is silver.

_____

h. Rewrite the sentence below in a shorter, more direct way. Use active voice. Hint: Put the last part of the sentence first.

These pictures were painted by the students.

_____

i. From memory, complete the chart that shows the structure of a typical five-paragraph essay.

```
┌──────────────────────────────────────┐
│  _____ Paragraph           │
│     1. _____       │
│     2. _____       │
└──────────────────────────────────────┘
┌──────────────────────────────────────┐
│  _____ Paragraph           │
│        _____ sentence      │
│     1. _____ sentence      │
│     2. _____ sentence      │
│     3. _____ sentence      │
└──────────────────────────────────────┘
┌──────────────────────────────────────┐
│  _____ Paragraph           │
│        _____ sentence      │
│     1. _____ sentence      │
│     2. _____ sentence      │
│     3. _____ sentence      │
└──────────────────────────────────────┘
┌──────────────────────────────────────┐
│  _____ Paragraph           │
│        _____ sentence      │
│     1. _____ sentence      │
│     2. _____ sentence      │
│     3. _____ sentence      │
└──────────────────────────────────────┘
┌──────────────────────────────────────┐
│  _____ Paragraph           │
│  1. Restatement of _____         │
│  2. Reference to each _____        │
│     _____                  │
│  3. _____                  │
└──────────────────────────────────────┘
```

36

LESSON 9

The Essay: Transitions

We have learned what is contained in an essay's three main parts: the introductory paragraph, the body paragraphs, and the concluding paragraph. Now, we can write a well-organized essay, yet our essay will be even better if we add **transitions** to connect paragraphs.

Transitions   A **transition** is a word, phrase, or clause that links one subject or idea to another. We place transitions at the beginning of paragraphs to help the essay "flow" from one paragraph to another. Transitions make the ideas easier for the reader to follow. Here are some typical transitions:

> *What is more,…*
>
> *On the other hand,…*
>
> *Despite all that,…*
>
> *In short,…*
>
> *As a result,…*
>
> *Another thing…*
>
> *The second reason…*
>
> *A final thing that makes…*
>
> *In addition to the other reasons,…*
>
> *In conclusion,…*

Transitions tell the reader these things:

- you are starting to support your thesis statement
- you are going to bring up a new point
- you are going to continue giving more information
- you are about to conclude your essay

Transitional words and phrases can appear anywhere in a sentence.

> *Roy, **too**, enjoys playing baseball.*
> *David enjoys cooking **as well**.*

37

Transitions will greatly improve your writing. Generally, you should have a transition at the beginning of every paragraph except for the first paragraph. Transitions linking paragraphs are underlined in the paragraphs below.

In addition, Tamika likes to swim in the lake. Sometimes, she swims all the way across the lake. Other times, she just floats on a raft. She also likes diving beneath the surface to see the fish …

Another thing she likes to do at the park is to play games. With her friends, she plays tag, soccer, and baseball …

Example Underline the transitional words in each sentence below.

(a) Furthermore, sand tiger sharks do not attack people.

(b) Lorena talked about the hammerhead, for example.

(c) To sum up, sharks vary in size, appearance, and behavior.

We underline transitional words as follows:

(a) **Furthermore**, sand tiger sharks do not attack people.

(b) Lorena talked about the hammerhead, **for example.**

(c) **To sum up,** sharks vary in size, appearance, and behavior.

Practice and Review Underline the transitional words in sentences a–c.

a. Alex reported on great white sharks, also.

b. Besides that, Alex drew a great white shark.

c. Alex, therefore, did extra work.

d. Underline the thesis statement in the introductory paragraph below.

Ms. Feelyne despises dogs and wants to add extra taxes to those who own dogs. She considers dogs a public nuisance because they bark constantly and leave messes everywhere. I disagree. I believe that more people should have dogs, for dogs offer companionship, protection, and fun.

e. Read the sentences below. Then, number them according to what happens first, next, etc. (Place numbers one through four in the boxes.)

☐ He fills a bucket with water and finds a large sponge.

☐ Moving the car onto the driveway, Ron decides to wash the car.

☐ He washes, rinses, and dries the car thoroughly.

☐ Ron moves the shiny car into the garage to keep it clean.

f. Underline the topic sentence in the paragraph below.

> Last week, Juan went to the library and checked out three books about sharks. Also, he read a magazine article about different kinds of whales. In the past, he has read stories about dolphins, crabs, and sea horses. His favorite story of all was about an octopus. Juan loves reading about sea creatures.

g. Draw a line through the sentence that does not belong in the paragraph below.

> Although many people fear the great white shark, it is actually the bull shark that is the most aggressive. Bull sharks hunt in the warm, shallow waters where people most often swim. Hammerheads have white bellies. Scientists believe that bull sharks mistake humans for big fish, for humans are not their preferred food.

For h and i, combine sentences to make one compact sentence.

h. Bull sharks eat fish. They eat dolphins and sea turtles, too.

_____

(review continued on next page)

i. This is a picture of a shark. It is a bull shark.

_____

j. Write the sentence below in a shorter, more direct way. Use active voice. Hint: Put the last part of the sentence first.

The hammerhead was attacked by a bull shark.

_____

k. From memory, complete the chart that shows the structure of a typical five-paragraph essay.

```
┌─────────────────────────────────────┐
│ _____ Paragraph           │
│     1. _____    │
│     2. _____    │
└─────────────────────────────────────┘
  ┌───────────────────────────────────┐
  │ _____ Paragraph         │
  │       _____ sentence    │
  │     1. _____ sentence   │
  │     2. _____ sentence   │
  │     3. _____ sentence   │
  └───────────────────────────────────┘
    ┌─────────────────────────────────┐
    │ _____ Paragraph       │
    │       _____ sentence  │
    │     1. _____ sentence │
    │     2. _____ sentence │
    │     3. _____ sentence │
    └─────────────────────────────────┘
      ┌───────────────────────────────┐
      │ _____ Paragraph       │
      │     _____ sentence  │
      │   1. _____ sentence │
      │   2. _____ sentence │
      │   3. _____ sentence │
      └───────────────────────────────┘
  ┌───────────────────────────────────┐
  │ _____ Paragraph         │
  │ 1. Restatement of _____        │
  │ 2. Reference to each _____        │
  │    _____                 │
  │ 3. _____                 │
  └───────────────────────────────────┘
```

40

LESSON 10

Brainstorming for Ideas

We have learned all the necessary parts of an essay, including transitions. In this lesson, we shall learn how to prepare to write a five-paragraph essay if we are given a thesis statement.

Brainstorming   **Brainstorming** is a method of quickly capturing ideas about a topic or problem. In this lesson, we shall brainstorm for ideas to create supporting paragraphs for a thesis statement. One way to brainstorm is illustrated below.

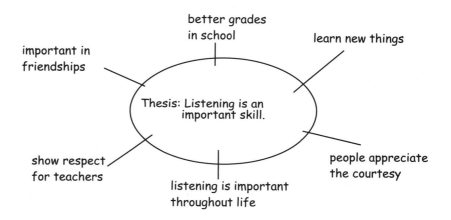

For the next few minutes, use this model to record brainstorming ideas for the thesis statement "Animals can teach people many things." You may use the worksheet on the following page. Quickly begin to write in the area outside the circle any and all words that come into your mind as soon as they come into your mind.

- Write quickly. Do not allow your pencil to stop moving.

- Do not worry about spelling or neatness.

- Do not worry about the word order or location.

- Do not think; just write.

Write for about three minutes or until your paper is covered with words, whichever comes first.

When you have finished, you will almost certainly have several ideas to help you get started writing your essay.

Brainstorming for Body Paragraph Ideas

Animals can teach people many things.

Organizing your Ideas   After you have brainstormed, the next step is to look at the ideas that you have generated and identify the ones that best support your thesis statement. Follow these steps to organize your ideas:

1. Take a moment to look at the words or groups of words that you wrote. Some of them will relate very well to the thesis, and others will look like they do not belong or are not as strong.

2. Choose at least three different words or groups of words that best support the thesis. Circle them. If you cannot decide on just three, you may circle four or five. If you circle more than three words or groups of words, you have more than enough support for your thesis statement. You can write several body paragraphs of support, or you can combine one or more arguments, and you can eliminate the weaker ones.

3. These circled word groups will become your *body paragraph ideas*. Write these ideas on the lines provided below (or type them into your computer file), leaving space underneath each idea to add more notes later for expanding the paragraphs.

4. Look at your *body paragraph ideas* and try to determine the order in which they should be arranged in the body of your essay to best support your thesis. Number the ideas. You can rearrange the order, eliminate unnecessary ideas, or add additional body paragraphs at any time as ideas come to you.

| # | | *Body paragraph idea:* _____ |

_____

_____

_____

_____

| # | | *Body paragraph idea:* _____ |

_____

_____

_____

_____

| # | *Body paragraph idea:* _____ |

_____

_____

_____

_____

| # | *Body paragraph idea:* _____ |

_____

_____

_____

_____

Forming Topic Sentences   Once you have selected the best ideas from your brainstorming and written them on the lines above, the next step is to take those ideas and form them into topic sentences. Each topic sentence will become a main idea for your essay's body paragraphs.

Practice   Write at least three topic sentences that clearly support your thesis statement. In Lesson 11, we shall expand these topic sentences into body paragraphs and then complete an essay.

Topic sentence: _____

_____

_____

Topic sentence: _____

_____

_____

Topic sentence: _____

_____

_____

Topic sentence: _____

_____

_____

44

Review   Underline the transitional words in sentences a–c.

    a.   Furthermore, mammals drink milk when they are young.

    b.   Birds, on the other hand, hatch from hard-shelled eggs.

    c.   Spiders and insects are grouped similarly.

    d.   Underline the topic sentence in the paragraph below.

        Animals with similar characteristics are grouped into classes. There are five classes of animals with backbones. These are called vertebrates. There are two common classes of animals without backbones. These are called invertebrates.

    e.   Draw a line through the sentence that does not belong in the paragraph below.

        Mammals are one class of animals with similar characteristics. Mammals are warm blooded and have hair. Mammals drink milk then they are babies. Spiders do not have backbones. Most mammals live inside their mothers before they are born. All mammals have backbones.

For f and g, combine sentences to make one compact sentence.

    f.   Birds have feathers. Birds have wings.

    _____

    g.   Bats have wings. Bats do not have feathers.

    _____

    h.   Write the sentence below in a shorter, more direct way. Use active voice. Hint: Put the last part of the sentence first.

        The animals were grouped by the students.

    _____

(review continued on next page)

i. From memory, complete the chart showing the structure of a typical five-paragraph essay.

> _____ Paragraph
> 1. _____
> 2. _____

> _____ Paragraph
> _____ sentence
> 1. _____ sentence
> 2. _____ sentence
> 3. _____ sentence

> _____ Paragraph
> _____ sentence
> 1. _____ sentence
> 2. _____ sentence
> 3. _____ sentence

> _____ Paragraph
> _____ sentence
> 1. _____ sentence
> 2. _____ sentence
> 3. _____ sentence

> _____ Paragraph
> 1. Restatement of _____
> 2. Reference to each _____
>   _____
> 3. _____

46

LESSON 11

Writing a Complete Essay

In Lesson 10, you brainstormed and created ideas to support the thesis statement "Animals can teach people many things." You also chose the best of those ideas and put them in the order that best supports the thesis statement. Then, you used the ideas to create topic sentences. Now, you are ready to write the complete essay.

Practice Using the topic sentences that you wrote for Lesson 10, follow the steps below to complete the essay.

1. For each topic sentence, write a body paragraph to support the thesis statement. To expand your paragraph, you might ask yourself *who, what, when, where, why,* and *how* questions. Your answers to these questions will give you ideas for supporting sentences.

2. Create an introductory paragraph with an introductory sentence (a "hook") that will grab the reader's interest, and a sentence that states the thesis.

3. Write a concluding paragraph that includes a restatement of the thesis, a reference to each of the topic sentences, and a clincher statement.

4. Add transitions between body paragraphs to make your ideas easier for the reader to follow. Pay special attention to the transition into the concluding paragraph.

5. Finally, put all the parts together to form a complete essay. As you are working, make any necessary corrections to your previous work. You might add or subtract words, or make any other change that results in a more effective essay. **Keep this essay in your three-ring binder.** You will evaluate it in the next lesson.

47

LESSON 12

Evaluating Your Essay

The Writing Process

All of the writing that we do should be viewed as "work in progress." Even after you have turned in an essay to your teacher for a grade, you should not feel that it can never be touched again. The knowledge that *writing is a process* should guide your thinking throughout the construction of an essay. From the first steps in organizing your thoughts, to creating body paragraphs, to adding transitions, you should feel free to make changes to improve your work.

At each step of the writing process, you should stop to re-evaluate both your thoughts and the words that you have placed on the page.

It is helpful to do this after each step of the writing process. It is also important to do this after the entire essay is written. In fact, it is probably most helpful to complete an essay, then walk away from it for a day or two, and then come back and read the essay again.

Many times, sentences that seemed good the first time appear much different a day or two later. Furthermore, you may find that more ideas have come to you, or ideas that were somewhat muddled before have become clearer. Two days later, you can write them in a way that is more meaningful to the reader.

Use the following guidelines to help you evaluate your writing.

Evaluating Your Writing

Do not be afraid to change what you have already written. Just because your essay was typed or written on paper in ink does not mean that it cannot be improved.

Ask yourself these questions throughout the writing process:

- Is my introductory sentence interesting? *If it is not interesting to you, it certainly will not be interesting to the reader.*

- Do I have a thesis statement that clearly explains the subject of this essay? (For this assignment, the thesis was given to you.)

- Does my thesis statement clearly state my position?

- Does each body paragraph have a clear topic sentence at the beginning that tells the subject of the paragraph? *Read each*

topic sentence without the rest of the paragraph to see if it can stand alone as a strong idea.

- Are there other sentences that I can add to help improve my credibility and help the reader to better understand my point?

- Have I described my emotions and feelings so well that they create a picture in the mind of the reader to help him or her feel the same as I feel?

- Does each paragraph (except for the first) begin with an effective transition?

- Are there other arguments that I can add as additional body paragraphs to help me prove my point?

- Are some of my arguments weak and unconvincing? Should they be removed because they do not help me prove my point?

- Do my body paragraphs appear in the best possible order to prove my point? Could I place them in a different order that is more logical or effective?

- Is each sentence constructed as well as it should be? *Read each sentence in each paragraph as if it were the only sentence on the page. This helps you to catch sentence fragments, run-on sentences, misspellings, and grammatical errors. If you are working on a computer, put blank lines between each sentence, so you actually only see one full sentence at a time on your screen. This will reveal sentence fragments to you.*

- Does my concluding paragraph summarize and reinforce the ideas and opinions expressed in the essay? Is there a reference to each topic sentence? Is there a clincher sentence?

Practice   Use the Evaluation Form on the following page to evaluate the essay that you wrote for Lesson 11. Read your essay carefully as you check for the items listed on the Evaluation Form. Write YES or NO in the blank next to each question.

When you are finished, you will either be confident that you have a strong essay, or you will know where it needs to be improved.

If you answered NO to one or more of the questions on the Evaluation Form, rewrite to improve those areas.

When you can answer YES to every question on the Evaluation Form, you will have completed this assignment.

49

Essay Evaluation Form

Thesis: _____

_____ Is my introductory sentence interesting? *If it is not interesting to you, it certainly will not be interesting to the reader.*

_____ Do I have a thesis statement that clearly explains the subject of this essay?

_____ Does my thesis statement clearly state my position?

_____ Does each body paragraph have a clear topic sentence at the beginning that tells the subject of the paragraph? *Read each topic sentence without the rest of the paragraph to see if it can stand alone as a strong idea.*

_____ Have I included sentences that improve my credibility and help the reader to better understand my point?

_____ Have I described my emotions and feelings so well that they create a picture in the mind of the reader to help him or her feel the same as I feel?

_____ Does each paragraph (except for the first paragraph) begin with an effective transition?

_____ Are there no other arguments that I can add as additional body paragraphs to help me prove my point?

_____ Are all of my arguments strong and convincing? Do they all help to prove my point?

_____ Do my body paragraphs appear in the best possible order to prove my point? Is their order logical and effective?

_____ Is each sentence structured as well as it could be? *Read each sentence in each paragraph as if it were the only sentence on the page. This helps you to catch fragments and run-on sentences.*

_____ Does my concluding paragraph summarize and reinforce the ideas and opinions expressed in the essay?

50

LESSON 13

Supporting a Topic Sentence with Experiences, Examples, Facts, and Opinions

We remember that supporting sentences support, prove, or explain the topic sentence of that paragraph. We have learned to use *who, what, when, where, why*, and *how* questions to come up with sentences to support a topic sentence. In this lesson, we shall discover additional ways to create supporting sentences.

Experiences Your **experiences,** or the experiences of other people, can strongly support a topic sentence. An experience sentence explains or illustrates an event that supports the topic sentence. Consider the experience sentences below:

> We students created a fact-filled bulletin board to help us remember the different classes of animals.

Examples Like experiences, **examples** can explain or illustrate events that help to prove, support, or explain your topic sentence. Consider the following example sentence:

> For example, birds have feathers and hatch from hard-shelled eggs.

Facts A **fact** is a piece of information that can be proven to be true. You can use a fact from research to support or prove your topic sentence. Consider the fact sentence below:

> Without feathers, bats cannot be classified as birds.

Experiences, examples, and facts are always the strongest arguments to prove a point, so they should immediately follow the topic sentence to build a strong paragraph.

Opinions Your **opinions** are your thoughts or feelings about a particular subject. Although a fact is something that can be proven true, an opinion is something that cannot be proven true or false. For example, it is a fact that cats are mammals. It is opinion to say that cats make better pets than dogs.

51

Opinion sentences, communicating thoughts and feelings that are directly related to the topic sentence, may follow experience, example, and fact sentences to further develop the body paragraph. Consider the opinion sentences below:

> Hammerhead sharks are the funniest-looking fish in the whole world.

> No skill is more important than listening.

> Bats are the most amazing creatures on the planet.

Example Use experience, example, fact, and opinion sentences to support the following topic sentence:

> The ant is a hard-working insect.

We can write the following sentences to support the topic sentence above:

> Experience sentence: Last summer, ants got into our kitchen, and some were carrying bread crumbs twice their size.

> Example sentence: For example, each ant in the colony has its own job to do.

> Fact sentence: Scientists say that an ant can lift twenty times its own weight.

> Opinion sentence: I think people can learn much from ants.

Practice and Review a. Write experience, example, fact, and opinion sentences to support this topic sentence:

With practice, people can improve their skills.

Experience sentence: _____

_____

_____

_____

52

Example sentence: _____

_____

_____

_____

Fact sentence: _____

_____

_____

_____

Opinion sentence: _____

_____

_____

_____

Underline the transitional words in sentences b–d.

b. First, Sam gathered all that he needed to bathe the dog.

c. His clothes, towels, and hair were soaked with water as a result.

d. Therefore, Ana wondered who really got the bath.

e. Underline the topic sentence in the paragraph below.

Another class of animals is fish. Scientists believe that there are more than 24,000 kinds of fish. Fish live in the water and come in many shapes and sizes. They have scales, fins, and gills. Most are cold-blooded.

(practice continued on next page)

f. Draw a line through the sentence that does not belong in the paragraph below.

Reptiles are another class of animals. They are cold-blooded and scaly. Unlike fish, reptiles live on land. Turtles, alligators, crocodiles, lizards, and snakes all belong to the reptile family. Some fish catch passing bugs by shooting a stream of water. Reptile scales can be hard or soft, large or small.

For g and h, combine sentences to make one compact sentence.

g. Kim held a snake. The snake was long and yellow.

_____

_____

h. Amphibians have lungs. Amphibians can live on land.

_____

_____

i. Write the sentence below in a shorter, more direct way. Use active voice. Hint: Put the last part of the sentence first.

The lizard was warmed by the sun.

_____

_____

(practice continued on next page)

j. From memory, complete the chart showing the structure of a typical five-paragraph essay.

_____ Paragraph
1. _____
2. _____

_____ Paragraph
_____ sentence
1. _____ sentence
2. _____ sentence
3. _____ sentence

_____ Paragraph
_____ sentence
1. _____ sentence
2. _____ sentence
3. _____ sentence

_____ Paragraph
_____ sentence
1. _____ sentence
2. _____ sentence
3. _____ sentence

_____ Paragraph
1. Restatement of _____
2. Reference to each _____
_____
3. _____

55

LESSON 14

Preparing to Write a Persuasive (Opinion) Essay

Four Purposes for Writing

Every piece of writing has a purpose. There are four basic purposes for writing: narrative, expository, descriptive, and persuasive.

Narrative writing tells a story or relates a series of events. A composition describing your trip to the local zoo would be narrative writing. In a later lesson, you will write a narrative essay telling about a personal experience of your choice.

Expository writing gives information about a topic or explains a subject. An article entitled "How Animals Are Grouped" would be an example of expository writing. Another example is your essay explaining how animals can teach people things.

Descriptive writing describes a person, place, or thing. Examples include a brochure describing a zoo, a personal composition about your special pet, and a "Mammal" poster that describes the characteristics of a mammal. Later, you will practice this type of writing by describing a person that you see often.

Persuasive writing attempts to convince someone to do or believe something. An advertisement for Mr. Follicle's Hair Growth Shampoo, an article about the importance of eating dark green vegetables, and a campaign flyer urging voters to vote for a certain person are all examples of persuasive writing. In this lesson, you will write a persuasive essay.

The Persuasive Essay

Remembering the structure of a complete essay, we shall prepare to write a persuasive essay using the following sentence as our thesis statement:

Students should be required to eat a healthy breakfast every morning.

The goal of this essay will be to convince or *persuade* the reader that students should be required to eat a healthy breakfast every morning.

56

Persuasive essays usually deal with controversial topics, subjects that have two sides. If you prefer, you may argue the opposite side and rewrite the thesis statement to read, "Students *should not* be required to eat a healthy breakfast every morning."

As you do your brainstorming for this exercise, you will see if there are enough strong arguments to support your thesis. This is why brainstorming before you write is such an important exercise. It saves you a great deal of time by convincing you that your thesis statement can or cannot be supported as well as giving you the main ideas for all of your topic sentences.

Your essay will prove that your thesis statement is correct. You will use several arguments to convince the reader of this.

Brainstorming

Brainstorming is always our first step in writing an essay. Recall that we draw a circle in the middle of a blank sheet of paper. Inside the circle, write the thesis statement. Then, quickly begin to write in the area outside the circle any and all words that come into your mind as soon as they come into your mind.

- Write quickly, and do not worry about spelling or neatness.

- Write for about three minutes or until your paper is covered with words, whichever comes first.

- As you write, continue to read your thesis statement in the middle of the circle. This will keep you focused.

Organizing your Ideas

After you have brainstormed, look at the ideas that you have generated and identify the ones that best support your thesis statement. Follow these steps to organize your ideas:

1. Take a moment to look at the words or groups of words that you wrote. Some of them will begin to surface as relating very well to the thesis; they will firmly argue your point and convince the reader. Others will begin to look as though they do not belong or are not as strong.

2. Choose at least three different words or groups of words that best support the thesis. Circle them. If you cannot decide on just three, you may circle four or five. If you circle more than three words or groups of words, you have more than enough support for your thesis statement. You can write several body paragraphs of support. Or, you

might combine one or more arguments and eliminate the weaker ones.

3. These circled word groups will become your *body paragraph ideas.* Write these ideas on a separate piece of paper leaving space underneath each idea to add more notes later for expanding the paragraphs.

4. Look at your body paragraph ideas and try to determine the order in which they should be arranged in the body of your essay to best support your thesis. Number the ideas. You can rearrange the order or even eliminate or add additional body paragraphs at any time as ideas come to you.

Forming Topic Sentences   Once you have selected the best ideas from your brainstorming and placed them on a separate page, take those ideas and form them into topic sentences. Each topic sentence will become a main idea for your essay's body paragraphs.

Practice   Write at least three topic sentences that clearly support your thesis statement. In Lesson 15, we shall develop these topic sentences into body paragraphs and then complete the persuasive essay.

Topic sentence: _____

_____

_____

Topic sentence: _____

_____

_____

Topic sentence: _____

_____

_____

Topic sentence: _____

_____

_____

58

LESSON
15

Writing the Persuasive (Opinion) Essay

In Lesson 14, you prepared to write your persuasive essay. By brainstorming, you gathered ideas. You chose the best of those ideas and put them in the order that best supports your thesis statement. Then, you used the ideas to create at least three topic sentences. Now, you are ready to write the complete essay.

Practice   Using the topic sentences that you wrote for Lesson 14, follow the steps below to complete the persuasive essay.

1. For each topic sentence, write a body paragraph to support the thesis statement. Refer back to Lessons 4 and 13 for different ways to expand a topic sentence into a paragraph. In addition to experience and opinion sentences, you might write definitions, examples, facts, or arguments that support the topic sentence.

2. Create an introductory paragraph and a concluding paragraph. Remember that the introductory sentence should grab the reader's interest and that the "last words" of your conclusion will leave a lasting impression.

3. Add transitions between body paragraphs to make your ideas easier for the reader to follow. Pay special attention to the transition into the concluding paragraph.

4. Finally, put all the parts together to form a complete essay. As you are working, make any necessary corrections to your previous work. You might add words, remove words, or make other changes that result in a more convincing, persuasive essay.

Additional Practice   (Optional) After you have evaluated your persuasive essay using the guidelines in Lesson 16, you might try writing another persuasive essay on one of the topics listed below. Choose "should" or "should not" to complete your thesis statement.

1. Parents (should, should not) buy cell phones for their middle-school students.

2. People (should, should not) be allowed to own dogs that have aggressive personalities.

3. My bedtime (should, should not) be an hour earlier than it is now.

4. People (should, should not) be allowed to own as many pets as they desire.

5. Students (should, should not) be allowed to talk as much as they want whenever they want.

LESSON 16

Evaluating the Persuasive (Opinion) Essay

We have learned that all of the writing that we do is "work in progress." The knowledge that *writing is a process* guides our thinking throughout the construction of an essay. From the first steps in organizing our thoughts, to creating body paragraphs, to adding transitions, we constantly make changes to improve our work.

At each step of the writing process, we should stop to re-evaluate both our thoughts and the words we have placed on the page.

Evaluating Your Writing

In Lesson 15, you completed your persuasive essay. Now that some time has passed, you are ready to evaluate it using the following guidelines.

Ask yourself these questions:

- Is my introductory sentence ("hook") interesting? *If it is not interesting to you, it certainly will not be interesting to the reader.*

- Does my thesis statement clearly state my position?

- Does each body paragraph have a clear topic sentence that tells the subject of the paragraph? *Read each topic sentence without the rest of the paragraph to see if it can stand alone as a strong idea.*

- Does each of my topic sentences strongly support my thesis statement?

- Are there other personal experiences, facts, examples, or arguments that I can add to help improve my credibility and help the reader to better understand my point?

- Have I described in my opinion sentences my emotions and feelings so well that they create a picture in the mind of the reader to help him or her feel the same as I feel?

- Does each paragraph (except for the first) begin with an effective transition?

- Are there other arguments that I can add as additional body paragraphs to help me prove my point?

- Are some of my arguments weak and unconvincing? Should they be removed because they do not help me prove my point?

- Do my body paragraphs appear in the best possible order to prove my point? Could I place them in a different order that is more logical or effective?

- Is each sentence constructed as well as it should be? *Read each sentence in each paragraph as if it were the only sentence on the page. This helps you to find and correct sentence fragments, run-on sentences, misspellings, and grammatical errors.*

- Does my concluding paragraph summarize and reinforce the ideas and opinions expressed in the essay? Have I convinced the reader that my thesis statement is true? Does my essay end with a powerful clincher sentence?

Practice Use the Evaluation Form on the page following this lesson to evaluate the persuasive essay that you wrote for Lesson 15. Read your essay carefully as you check for the items listed on the Evaluation Form. Write YES or NO in the blank next to each question.

When you are finished, you will either be confident that you have a strong essay, or you will know where it needs to be improved.

If you answered NO to one or more of the questions on the Evaluation Form, rewrite to improve those areas.

When you can answer YES to every question on the Evaluation Form, you will have completed this assignment.

62

Persuasive Essay Evaluation Form

Thesis: _____

_____ Is my introductory sentence interesting? *If it is not interesting to you, it certainly won't be interesting to the reader.*

_____ Do I have a thesis statement that clearly explains the subject of this essay?

_____ Does my thesis statement clearly state my position?

_____ Does each body paragraph have a clear topic sentence at the beginning that tells the subject of the paragraph? *Read each topic sentence without the rest of the paragraph to see if it can stand alone as a strong idea.*

_____ Are there no other experiences, facts, or examples that I can add to help improve my credibility and help the reader to better understand my point?

_____ Have I described in my opinion sentences my emotions and feelings so well that they create a picture in the mind of the reader to help him or her feel the same as I feel?

_____ Does each paragraph (except for the first paragraph) begin with an effective transition?

_____ Are there no other arguments that I can add as additional body paragraphs to help me prove my point?

_____ Are all of my arguments strong and convincing?

_____ Do my body paragraphs appear in the best possible order to prove my point?

_____ Is each sentence structured as well as it could be? *Read each sentence in each paragraph as if it were the only sentence on the page. This helps you to catch fragments and run-on sentences.*

_____ Does my concluding paragraph summarize and reinforce the ideas and opinions expressed in the essay?

63

LESSON 17   Writing a Strong Thesis Statement

The Thesis Statement The thesis statement clearly states the subject of the entire essay. We have practiced writing a complete essay based on an assigned thesis statement. In this lesson, we shall practice creating our own thesis statements for assigned topics.

We remember that the thesis statement states not only the subject of the essay but also the writer's position on the topic.

Brainstorming When faced with an assigned topic, we prepare by brainstorming to generate ideas and thoughts.

The first step in brainstorming is choosing your direction. You would not get into a car and just begin to drive, expecting to arrive at nowhere in particular. You need to know where you are going before you pull out of the driveway. In other words, you must think about the topic, choose your direction or focus.

For example, if the assignment is to write about the qualities that make a good student, your thesis statement could begin, "The qualities that make a good student are …"

After brainstorming about the topic, perhaps you have decided that there are four specific qualities that make a good student. If so, your thesis statement might be the following:

There are four important qualities that make a good student.

Practice Below are ten topics that could be given to you as subjects for essays. For each topic, brainstorm briefly. Then, write a declarative sentence that could be used as a strong thesis statement for a complete essay.

1. The best things about the city or county in which you live

_____

_____

2. The qualities that make a true friend

_____

_____

64

3. Why a person should get enough sleep

_____

_____

4. Things that you would change about your country if you were President

_____

_____

5. What you will accomplish this school year that you did not last school year

_____

_____

6. Some ways that you can save water

_____

_____

7. Some events that you will always remember

_____

_____

8. What you can do to take better care of your body

_____

_____

65

LESSON 18

Developing an Outline

Developing an Outline

An outline can help us to organize our ideas in a logical manner. In this lesson, we shall review the basic outline form and practice developing an outline in preparation for writing future essays or research papers.

Outline Form

An outline is a list of topics and subtopics arranged in an organized form. We use Roman numerals for main topics. For subtopics, we use uppercase letters. For a very detailed outline, we use alternating numbers as shown below.

Title

I. Main topic

    A. Subtopic of I

    B. Subtopic of I

        1. Subtopic of B

        2. Subtopic of B

            a. Subtopic of 2

            b. Subtopic of 2

                (1) Subtopic of b

                (2) Subtopic of b

II. Main topic

    A. Subtopic of II…etc.

Notice that we indent subtopics so that all letters and numbers of the same kind are directly under one another. Notice also that we use **at least two subdivisions** (letters or numbers of the same kind) for each category.

Topic Outline

An outline may be either a topic or a sentence outline. In a topic outline, each main topic or subtopic is written as a single word or phrase. On the next page is an example of a topic outline for the first part of an essay about using time wisely.

66

Maximizing Minutes

I. Importance of using time wisely

   A. To give a sense of accomplishment
   B. To fulfill responsibilities

II. Difficulties in using time wisely

   A. One's own desires
   B. Other activities

Sentence Outline   In a sentence outline, each topic is expressed as a complete sentence. Notice how the sentence outline below communicates more meaning than the short phrases of the topic outline.

Maximizing Minutes

I. Using time wisely is important.

   A. Students experience a sense of accomplishment when they use their time wisely.
   B. To fulfill their responsibilities, students must use their time wisely.

II. Wise use of time can be difficult.

   A. Sometimes a student would rather not do a certain task.
   A. A student might rather watch TV or make a phone call.

Practice   On a separate piece of paper, practice developing a topic outline by organizing the following set of information. You may work with your teacher or with a group of students.

Hint: First, look carefully over the list. You will find one main topic (I.) and two subtopics (A., B.). The rest of the items will be subtopics of subtopics (1., 2., 3.,...). You might begin by circling the main topic and underlining the two subtopics.

green beans	apples
cherries	peas
fresh produce	watermelons
squash	vegetables
fruits	plums
corn	grapes

*There is more than one way to develop this outline. After you have completed your outline, compare it to the "example outline" found on the last few pages of this Writing Packet.

Additional Practice

a. For Lesson 11, you wrote a complete essay containing at least three body paragraphs. Create a topic outline covering the body paragraphs of that essay. Hint: The topic sentence of each body paragraph will become a word or phrase beside a Roman numeral indicating a main topic in your outline. Therefore, your outline will have at least three Roman numerals.

b. For Lesson 15, you wrote a persuasive essay containing at least three body paragraphs. Create a topic outline for this essay.

68

LESSON 19

Preparing to Write an Expository (Informative) Essay

The purpose of expository writing is to inform or explain. Expository writing tells why or how. The following might be titles for expository essays:

> "How to Make Nutritious Granola"
>
> "New Phone Technology"
>
> "Where to Find Inexpensive Books"
>
> "Why Family Is Important"
>
> "Making a Yummy Grilled Cheese Sandwich"

A good expository essay is well organized and clear. It might offer an explanation of how something works, information about a specific subject, or instructions for doing something. You may want to include relevant facts, concrete details, quotations, or examples.

In this lesson, we shall prepare to write an expository essay that explains how to plan a camping trip.

Our goal is to write easy-to-follow instructions, which will require a detailed description of the process. Therefore, we shall break down the actions and carefully sequence them in a logical or practical order so that the reader can understand our step-by-step method of planning a camping trip.

Brainstorming To generate thoughts and ideas, we shall brainstorm before creating a thesis statement for our *how-to* essay.

- Write quickly, and do not worry about spelling or neatness.

- Write for about three minutes or until your paper is covered with words, whichever comes first.

Writing a Thesis Statement Now, it is time to state the purpose of your essay in a clear thesis statement. Using the ideas you have written by brainstorming, write a sentence that tells the subject of your essay.

Hint: Will you be presenting a certain number of *steps* in your how-to essay? Or, will you be explaining a number of different *parts* of a camping trip that need to be planned? Your thesis statement will reveal your presentation plan.

69

Organizing your Ideas After you have written a strong thesis statement telling the subject of your essay, look at the ideas you have generated by brainstorming and identify the ones that best support your thesis statement. Then, you might create thought clusters based on the ideas you generated while brainstorming. You should have at least three of these clusters in order to create your body paragraphs. Create a topic outline to organize your ideas.

Tone The **tone** of an essay reflects the writer's attitude toward the topic. Your attitude can be formal or informal, serious or silly, admiring or critical. An expository essay should be objective, presenting facts rather than opinions. Before you begin writing, you must decide on your tone.

Forming Topic Sentences Once you have decided on your tone, selected the main ideas from your brainstorming, arranged them in clusters, and developed an outline, take your main topics and form them into topic sentences. Each topic sentence will become a main idea for your essay's body paragraphs.

Practice Write a thesis statement and at least three topic sentences that clearly explain your thesis statement. In the next lesson, we shall develop these topic sentences into body paragraphs and then complete the expository essay.

THESIS STATEMENT: _____

_____

_____

Topic sentence: _____

_____

_____

Topic sentence: _____

_____

_____

Topic sentence: _____

_____

70

LESSON 20

Writing the Expository (Informative) Essay

In Lesson 19, you prepared to write your expository essay about how to plan a camping trip. By brainstorming, you gathered ideas and wrote a thesis statement. You chose the best of those ideas and put them into clusters. Then, you used the main ideas to create at least three topic sentences. Now, you are ready to write the complete essay.

Practice Using the topic sentences that you wrote for Lesson 19, follow the steps below to complete the expository essay.

1. For each topic sentence, write a body paragraph to support the thesis statement. Refer to your notes or outline and use the ideas underneath each Roman numeral to write body sentences that further explain, or expand, each topic sentence.

2. Create an introductory paragraph. Remember that the introductory sentence ("hook") should grab the reader's interest. Your thesis statement will clearly state the subject of the essay.

3. Create a concluding paragraph that refers to each topic sentence in your body paragraphs. Remember that the "last words" of your conclusion will leave a lasting impression.

4. Add transitions between body paragraphs to make your ideas easier for the reader to follow. Transitions that indicate order, such as "the first step..." or "the second step...," are appropriate in a how-to essay. Pay special attention to the transition into the concluding paragraph. Look back at Lesson 9 for help with transitions.

5. Finally, put all the parts together to form a complete essay. Use appropriate links to join connected ideas within your essay. As you are working, make any necessary corrections to your previous work. You might add things, remove things, or make other changes that result in a clearer, easier-to-follow expository essay.

Additional Practice (Optional) After you have evaluated your expository essay using the guidelines in Lesson 20, you might try writing

another expository essay on a topic of your choice or on one of these topics:

1. Explain how to play a game, any game that you know how to play.

2. Write an essay giving at least three reasons why you are thankful for your family.

3. Give instructions for caring for a pet.

4. Explain in detail how one might prepare a classroom for the first day of school.

5. Compare and contrast an alligator and a crocodile.

6. Tell how to construct a paper airplane, a model car, or another craft of your choice.

7. Compare and contrast the typical preschool child with a typical fourth-grade student.

8. Explain how three people have helped you to become the person that you are.

72

LESSON 21

Evaluating the Expository (Informative) Essay

We remember that all of our writing is "work in progress." The knowledge that *writing is a process* guides our thinking throughout the construction of an essay. Throughout the steps of brainstorming, organizing our thoughts, creating body paragraphs, and adding transitions, we constantly make changes to improve our work.

Evaluating Your Writing
In Lesson 20, you completed your expository essay. Now that some time has passed, you are ready to evaluate your essay using the following guidelines.

Ask yourself these questions:

- Is my introductory sentence ("hook") interesting? *If it is not interesting to you, it certainly will not be interesting to the reader.*

- Does my thesis statement clearly state the subject of my essay?

- Does each body paragraph have a clear topic sentence that provides the subject of the paragraph? *Read each topic sentence without the rest of the paragraph to see if it can stand alone as a strong idea.*

- Does each of my topic sentences strongly support my thesis statement?

- Are there other concrete details, facts, examples, or steps, that I can add to help improve my explanation or help the reader to better follow my instructions?

- Have I defined all technical terms and subject-specific vocabulary in my essay?

- Are my sentences in a logical or practical order?

- Does each paragraph (except for the first) begin with an effective transition?

- Are there other details that I can add as additional body paragraphs to create a fuller or clearer explanation?

73

- Are some of my sentences weak or confusing? Should they be removed because they do not help me to explain my topic?

- Do my body paragraphs appear in the best possible order? Could I place them in a different order that is more logical or effective?

- Is each sentence constructed as well as it should be? *Read each sentence in each paragraph as if it were the only sentence on the page. This helps you to catch sentence fragments, run-on sentences, misspellings, and grammatical errors.*

- Does my concluding paragraph summarize and reinforce the ideas expressed in the essay? Have I written a powerful clincher?

Practice Use the Evaluation Form on the page following this lesson to evaluate the expository essay you wrote for Lesson 12. Read your essay carefully as you check for the items listed on the Evaluation Form. Write YES or NO in the blank next to each question.

When you are finished, you will either be confident that you have a strong essay, or you will know where it needs to be improved.

If you answered NO to one or more of the questions on the Evaluation Form, rewrite to improve those areas.

When you can answer YES to every question on the Evaluation Form, you will have completed this assignment.

74

Expository Essay Evaluation Form

Thesis: _____

_____ Is my introductory sentence interesting? *If it is not interesting to you, it certainly will not be interesting to the reader.*

_____ Do I have a thesis statement that clearly explains the subject of this essay?

_____ Does my thesis statement clearly state my method of presentation?

_____ Does each body paragraph have a clear topic sentence that states the subject of the paragraph? *Read each topic sentence without the rest of the paragraph to see if it can stand alone as a strong idea.*

_____ Have I included every detail, fact, or example that I can to help improve my explanation and help the reader to better understand my point?

_____ Within each paragraph, are my sentences in a logical or practical order?

_____ Does each paragraph (except for the first paragraph) begin with an effective transition?

_____ Are there no other ideas that I can add as additional body paragraphs to create a fuller or clearer explanation?

_____ Are all of my sentences strong and clear? Do they all help me to explain?

_____ Do my body paragraphs appear in the best possible order? Is their order logical and effective?

_____ Is each sentence structured as well as it could be? *Read each sentence in each paragraph as if it were the only sentence on the page. This helps you to catch sentence fragments and run-on sentences.*

_____ Does my concluding paragraph summarize and reinforce each main idea expressed in the essay?

1. The first time I rode a horse in my life.

★ 2. When I almost cut my toe off and had to get twenty stiches.

3. When we went to Hawaii and I didn't want to swim with turtles.

★ 4. I was carrying a brush and my sister scared me and I threw the brush at her.

5. When my family and I were at a water park and I bought a snow cone and dropped it.

75

Preparing to Write a Personal Narrative

LESSON 22

Personal Narrative

Narrative writing tells a story or relates a series of events. In a **personal narrative,** the writer tells a story about a significant personal experience or event.

In this lesson, you will prepare to write a personal narrative in which you will share your feelings about how an experience affected you or taught you something.

Because this will be a personal narrative—a story that happened to you—you will be writing in what is called "the first person." Writing in the first person is just as if you were telling one of your friends about something that happened to you at the park yesterday. You will be using "I" and "we," and you can include action, suspense, vivid description, and even dialogue.

Choosing a Personal Experience

To think of an experience for a personal narrative that you would like to share, consider the following:

• a wonderful (or disastrous) first time that you did something

• a memorable struggle or hardship that you experienced

• a "turning point" in your life

• an interesting, exciting, humorous, or moving event in your life

• an unusual or once-in-a-life-time experience, such as touring a distant country, meeting a famous person, or making an amazing discovery

Reading through the daily journals that you have written might give you additional ideas.

Brainstorming

On a piece of scratch paper, quickly write every experience that comes to your mind. When you have finished, select the one that you think is most interesting, and write it on another piece of paper.

After selecting the experience that you plan to write about in your personal narrative, begin brainstorming in order to recall details or emotions about this experience. List all

Stiching a toe

Begining

- Tempe Market place / really hot. *on a weekend.*

- characters: Me, Mom, Maggey, Lisa

- Going to get cool → in water *doctor*
shoot-ups

Middle:

- We ran to shoot-ups got soaking wet

- I ran threw a sprinkler

- I fell and grabbed my knee
my mom called me over and
my toe was bleading.

End

- We rushed to the hospital.
- The gave me twenty stiches. *docotor*
- Then we went home and we
iced it and I had crutches.

words and phrases that come to mind. Without concern for spelling or grammar, write everything that occurs to you.

Organizing your Information

Once you have gathered your thoughts and memories, begin to plan your narrative by organizing the events in a logical order, which might be chronological order—the sequence in which the events occurred. Your rough plan might look something like this:

First: I rescued a dog from a busy highway, and …

Then: The dog wiggled as I tried to read the license tag hooked to its collar, and…

Then: I identified the dog's owner from the tag and called the owner …

Finally: The dog's owner came to my home to pick up the dog.

Using Accurate Verbs and Tenses

In a narrative essay, we use a variety of verbs and tenses to convey different times, sequences, and conditions accurately. You have learned to use past, present, and future tenses along with helping verbs to create precise meaning (he *must…*, she *might…*, they *should…*, etc.).

Modal Verbs

There are special types of helping verbs called **modal verbs.** The most common modal verbs are *can, could, may, might, must, shall, should, will,* and *would.*

We use *can* for general ability (present tense): Molly *can* do ten push-ups now. We use *may* for formal permission: Yes, you *may* borrow my pen. We use *could* for general ability (past tense): Molly *could* do four push-ups when she was six.

Let us consider the following sentences:

(a) (May, Can) I play outside?

(b) (Can, Could) Sun Min speak five languages when she was only ten years old?

(c) According to the law, we (would, should) wear seat belts in the car.

We complete the sentences as follows:

(a) **May** I play outside? (permission)

(b) **Could** Sun Min speak five languages when she was only ten years old? (general ability, past tense)

(c) According to the law, we **should** wear seat belts in the car. (We might not choose to wear them, but we *should*.)

Perfect Tenses You have practiced the four principal parts of both regular and irregular verbs, which are the tools you need to form other verb tenses, such as the perfect tenses.

The perfect tenses show that an action has been completed or "perfected." To form these tenses, we add a form of the helping verb *have* to the past participle.

Present Perfect The present perfect tense describes an action that occurred in the past and is complete or continuing in the present. We add the present forms of the verb *have* to the past participle.

PRESENT PERFECT TENSE = HAVE OR HAS + PAST PARTICIPLE

Edwin <u>has located</u> the owner of the dog.

I <u>have returned</u> the dog to its owner.

Past Perfect The past perfect tense describes past action completed before another past action. We use the helping verb *had* before the past participle.

PAST PERFECT TENSE = HAD + PAST PARTICIPLE

Kenny <u>had watered</u> the seeds already.

Birds <u>had eaten</u> many of them.

Future Perfect The future perfect tense describes future action to be completed before another future action. We add the future form of the helping verb *have* to the past participle.

FUTURE PERFECT TENSE = WILL HAVE OR SHALL HAVE + PAST PARTICIPLE

Isabel <u>will have completed</u> the quilt by December.

We <u>shall have written</u> many essays before the school year ends.

Notice that we use the past participle and not the past tense to form the perfect tenses:

She <u>has *drawn*</u> (not *drew*)....

He <u>had *gone*</u> (not *went*)....

They <u>will have *taken*</u> (not *took*)....

78

Practice Following the examples above, complete the sentences below using perfect tenses.

1. Heather (past perfect of *drive*) many miles that day.

_____

_____

2. Jasper (present perfect of *wear*) that shirt twice.

_____

_____

3. By noon, we (future perfect of *finish*) the job.

_____

_____

Practice For your personal narrative, write a rough plan similar to the one on the second page of this lesson. In the next lesson, you will expand each part of this plan into a paragraph and complete your narrative by filling in detail, action, and dialogue. Use a variety of accurate verbs and tenses to make your essay more precise and interesting.

First: _____

_____

Then:_____

_____

Then: _____

_____

Then: _____

_____

Finally: _____

_____

_____

LESSON 23 — Writing a Personal Narrative

In Lesson 22, you chose an interesting personal experience and created a rough plan for writing a personal narrative. In this lesson, you will use your rough plan and any other notes and begin writing your narrative.

Opening Paragraph Remember that your opening paragraph should capture the interest of the reader and establish your tone, which reveals your feelings or attitudes about the experience. You will write in first person, using the pronoun *I* or *we*.

Body Paragraphs Although you have a plan to follow, you may alter it as you write. Following the opening paragraph, each "then" part of your rough plan might become the topic sentence for a body paragraph in which you fill in details, actions, and any necessary dialogue.

Concluding Paragraph Your concluding paragraph will include a personal summary or commentary about how the experience affected you or taught you something significant.

Practice Write your personal narrative according to the guidelines above. Include an opening paragraph, two or more body paragraphs, and a concluding paragraph.

LESSON 24

Evaluating the Personal Narrative

All of our writing is "work in progress." The knowledge that *writing is a process* guides our thinking throughout the construction of our personal narrative. From the first steps in selecting an experience to share, to organizing our thoughts, to creating body paragraphs, to adding transitions, we constantly make changes to improve our work.

Evaluating Your Writing

In Lesson 23, you completed your personal narrative. Now that some time has passed, you are ready to evaluate it using the following guidelines.

Ask yourself these questions:

- Is my introductory sentence ("hook") interesting? *If it is not interesting to you, it certainly will not be interesting to the reader.*

- Does the beginning of the narrative clearly establish the tone?

- Does each body paragraph have a clear topic sentence that states the subject of the paragraph? *Read each topic sentence without the rest of the paragraph to see if it can stand alone as a strong idea.*

- Is the first-person point of view consistently maintained throughout the narrative?

- Are there other details, descriptions, emotions, or dialogue I could add to make a more interesting narrative?

- Are my sentences in a logical or chronological order? Have I used a variety of time-related terms to order the events?

- Does each paragraph (except for the first) begin with an effective transition?

- Are there other details that I can add as additional body paragraphs to create a fuller or more complete narrative?

- Are some of my sentences weak or confusing? Should they be removed because they do not relate to the story?

- Do my body paragraphs appear in the best possible order? Could I place them in a different order that is more logical or effective?

- Is each sentence constructed as well as it should be? *Read each sentence in each paragraph as if it were the only sentence on the page. This helps you to catch sentence fragments, run-on sentences, misspellings, and grammatical errors.*

- Does my concluding paragraph contain a summary or commentary about how the experience affected me?

Practice   Use the Evaluation Form on the page following this lesson to evaluate the personal narrative that you wrote for Lesson 20. Read your narrative carefully as you check for the items listed on the Evaluation Form. Write YES or NO in the blank next to each question.

When you are finished, you will either be confident that you have a strong personal narrative, or you will know where it needs to be improved.

If you answered NO to one or more of the questions on the Evaluation Form, rewrite to improve those areas.

When you can answer YES to every question on the Evaluation Form, you will have completed this assignment.

82

Personal Narrative Evaluation Form

Title: _____

_____ Is my introductory sentence ("hook") interesting? *If it is not interesting to you, it certainly will not be interesting to the reader.*

_____ Does the beginning of the narrative clearly establish the tone?

_____ Is the first-person point of view consistently maintained throughout the narrative?

_____ Does each body paragraph have a clear topic sentence that states the subject of the paragraph? *Read each topic sentence without the rest of the paragraph to see if it can stand alone as a strong idea.*

_____ Do the details all contribute to the reader's understanding of my personal experience?

_____ Within each paragraph, are my sentences in a logical or practical order?

_____ Does each paragraph (except for the first paragraph) begin with an effective transition?

_____ Are there no other details that I can add as additional body paragraphs to create a fuller or more complete narrative?

_____ Are all of my sentences strong and clear? Do they all directly relate to the story?

_____ Do my body paragraphs appear in the best possible order? Is their order logical and effective?

_____ Is each sentence structured as well as it could be? *Read each sentence in each paragraph as if it were the only sentence on the page. This helps you to catch sentence fragments and run-on sentences.*

_____ Does my concluding paragraph contain a personal summary or commentary about how the experience affected me or taught me something?

83

LESSON 25   Preparing to Write a Descriptive Essay

Descriptive writing describes a person, place, object, or event. With language that appeals to the senses, descriptive writing creates pictures in the reader's mind. Strong, vivid, and precise words are essential in creating clear descriptions.

In this lesson, we shall discuss the use of modifiers, comparisons, and sensory expressions to create accurate and complete descriptions. Then, you will prepare to write a descriptive essay about a person whom you can observe as you are writing.

Modifiers   To add detail, we can use modifiers—adjectives and adverbs; phrases and clauses. Modifiers supply additional information, making nouns and verbs more specific and precise.

> *Firmly* but *kindly*, my teacher made *many red* marks on my *long, wordy* essay.

In the English language, writers often use more than one adjective before a noun. For example, one might write, "The girl owned the *little brown* dog." When there is more than one adjective, the adjectives must be listed in the right order. Here is the proper order for adjectives:

1. descriptor: *a, an, the*

2. opinion: what you think about something (*foul* smell)

3. size: how big or small something is (*enormous* beast)

4. age: how old or young something is (*ancient* statue)

5. shape: the shape of something (*round* apple)

6. color: what the color of something is (*yellow* flower)

7. origin: where something came from (*Italian* shoes)

8. material: what something is made of (*wooden* doll)

9. purpose: what purpose something serves (*sleeping* bag)

10. noun

84

Example an (descriptor) ugly (opinion), huge (size),
antique (age), rectangle (shape), blond (color),
French (origin), oak (material), dining (purpose) table

On the lines provided, practice placing adjectives in the correct order:

a. Use the following adjectives to describe a book: a, English, thick, large

<u>a, large, thick, English</u> book

b. Use the following adjectives to describe a pan: an, roasting, aluminum, old

<u>an, old, aluminum, roasting</u> pan

c. Use the following adjectives to describe a towel: an, grey, beach, ugly

<u>an, ugly, grey, beach</u> towel

Check your answers with those in the Appendix.

Comparisons In addition to modifiers, we can use comparisons to make a description more vivid. *Simile* and *metaphor* are two kinds of comparisons. A **simile** expresses similarity between two things by using the word *like* or *as*:

> *Like a hen gathering her chicks,* the mother collected her adventurous children.

A **metaphor**, on the other hand, describes one thing as though it were another thing:

> Instinctively protecting, the mother *was a hen* with her children.

Both comparisons, simile and metaphor, help the reader to see a fuller picture of the mother collecting her children.

Sensory Expressions To create a more vivid image, we can appeal to the reader's five senses by detailing things that one can see, hear, smell, taste, and touch. For example, we can hear a donkey *bray,* see a star *twinkle,* smell the *fragrance* of a flower, feel the *roughness* of a brick wall, and taste the *sweetness* of a ripe orange.

85

Below, Frances Hodgson Burnett uses details, modifiers, and comparisons to describe Mary Lennox in her novel *A Secret Garden.*

> When Mary Lennox was sent to Misselthwaite Manor to live with her uncle, everybody said she was the <u>most disagreeable-looking child</u> ever seen. It was true, too. She had a <u>little thin</u> face and a <u>little thin</u> body, <u>thin light</u> hair and a <u>sour</u> expression.... She was a <u>sickly fretful, ugly little</u> baby ... and a <u>sickly, fretful toddling thing</u> .... By the time she was six years old she was a <u>tyrannical</u> and <u>selfish a little pig</u> as ever lived.

Frances Hodgson Burnett uses a metaphor to describe how Mary Lennox behaved when she arrived at her uncle's home:

> she was a tyrannical and selfish a little <u>pig</u> as ever lived.

In *The Wonderful Wizard of Oz,* Frank L. Baum creates a simile, comparing a house to the grayness all around Dorothy:

> And now the house was <u>as dull and gray as everything else</u>.

In his poem, "Fireflies," Paul Fleishman uses similes and metaphors to describe fireflies and their surroundings:

> Light is the ink we use [metaphor].
>
> Signing the June nights as if they were paintings [simile].

The examples above show how authors can create vivid pictures using details, modifiers, comparisons, and sensory expressions.

Correlative Conjunctions

Correlative conjunctions connect elements of a sentence that are equal in form, or parallel. Always used in pairs, they join similar words to words, phrases to phrases, or clauses to clauses. Here we list the most common ones:

both—and	either—or
neither—nor	not only—but also

When used correctly, correlative conjunctions can enhance our descriptions. Equal parts, or parallel elements, are italicized in the sentences below.

> Josh likes **not only** *hiking and sports* **but also** *books and music.*
>
> **Both** *cheerful* **and** *kind,* Vanna made friends easily.
>
> Adolf the dog has **neither** *a shiny coat* **nor** *a docile personality.*
>
> **Either** *Van is fast asleep* **or** *he is not home.*

86

Correlative conjunctions must join similar parts:

No: Julin is **both** clever, **and** she plays the piano well.
[joins an adjective and a clause]

Yes: Julin is **both** clever **and** musical.
[joins two adjectives]

No: **Either** she hid it **or** lost it.
[joins a clause and a phrase]

Yes: **Either** she hid it, **or** she lost it.
[joins two clauses]

Yes: She **either** hid it **or** lost it.
[joins two phrases]

No: Jerry enjoys **neither** swimming **nor** to color.
[joins a noun and a phrase]

Yes: Jerry enjoys **neither** swimming **nor** coloring.
[joins two nouns]

Consider using correlative conjunctions to create a more interesting descriptive essay.

Brainstorming   After choosing one person whom you can observe as you write, you are ready to begin brainstorming in order to gather precise and concrete details that will appeal to the reader's senses and fully describe that person.

You might want to consider these aspects of the person:

1. Physical appearance—size, age, gender; colors, shapes, hair texture, eyes, skin, and clothing; peculiar features or facial expressions; movements and gestures

2. Personality traits—mannerisms, habits, usual disposition. By their actions, people may demonstrate that they are intense or relaxed, hyperactive or plodding, outgoing or shy, humble or proud, etc.

3. How the person affects others and the world around him or her—Where does the person live? What does the person do? What are his or her passions or interests? How does he

or she relate to others? How does this person make you or other people feel?

On a blank piece of paper, quickly write everything that comes to your mind concerning the person that you wish to describe. Without regard for spelling or grammar, write all the nouns, verbs, adjectives, adverbs, phrases, clauses, comparisons, and sensory expressions that occur to you.

Organizing your Information Once you have gathered your thoughts and observations, begin to plan your descriptive essay by grouping the words and phrases into clusters. You might have one cluster of words and phrases that describe the person's physical appearance, another cluster focusing on the person's personality, and another telling about what the person does and/or how the person affects others and the world around him or her.

You can use each idea cluster to develop a topic sentence for each body paragraph in your essay.

Thesis Statement In your essay, you will be describing many different aspects of one person. What is the main impression you want your reader to receive concerning this person? Your thesis statement will sum up that which is most important.

<u>Practice</u> For your descriptive essay, write a thesis statement and three or more topic sentences about the person that you wish to describe. In the next lesson, you will develop each topic sentence into a body paragraph by adding more detail. Keep your brainstorming paper and this assignment in your three-ring binder so that you will be ready to complete your essay.

THESIS STATEMENT: _____

_____

_____

Topic sentence: _____

_____

Topic sentence: _____

_____

Topic sentence: _____

_____

_____

89

LESSON 26

Writing a Descriptive Essay

In Lesson 25, you prepared to write your descriptive essay about a person of your choice. By brainstorming, you gathered ideas and details. Then, you organized those details into clusters representing main ideas. From those clusters, you created a thesis statement and at least three topic sentences. Now, you are ready to write the complete essay.

Practice Using the topic sentences that you wrote for Lesson 25, follow the steps below to complete the descriptive essay.

1. Develop each topic sentence into a body paragraph, remembering your thesis. Refer to your brainstorming notes and idea clusters to write body sentences that add more detail and create a vivid picture in the reader's mind.

2. Create an introductory paragraph and a concluding paragraph. Remember that the introductory sentence ("hook") should grab the reader's interest and that the "last words" (clincher) of your conclusion will leave a lasting impression.

3. Add a variety of effective transitions between body paragraphs to make your ideas easier for the reader to follow. Pay special attention to the transition into the concluding paragraph.

4. Finally, combine all the parts to form a complete essay. As you are working, make any necessary corrections to your previous work. You might add things, remove things, or make other changes that result in a clearer, fuller descriptive essay.

Additional Practice (Optional) After you have evaluated your descriptive essay using the guidelines in Lesson 27, you might try writing another descriptive essay on a topic of your choice or on one of these topics:

1. A character from a novel that you have read

2. An item in your school or home

3. A pet or an animal that interests you

4. Your favorite place to go

5. Your favorite day of the year

90

LESSON 27

Evaluating the Descriptive Essay

Because *writing is a process* and all of our writing is "work in progress," we constantly make changes to improve our work.

Evaluating Your Writing

In Lesson 26, you completed your descriptive essay. Now that some time has passed, you are ready to evaluate it using the following guidelines.

Ask yourself these questions:

• Is my introductory sentence ("hook") interesting? *If it is not interesting to you, it certainly will not be interesting to the reader.*

• Does the thesis statement focus on a single person, place, object, or event?

• Does the thesis statement give my main impression of the person, place, object, or event that I am describing?

• Does each body paragraph have a clear topic sentence that states the subject of the paragraph? *Read each topic sentence without the rest of the paragraph to see if it can stand alone as a strong idea.*

• Are there other details, modifiers, comparisons, or sensory expressions that I could add to help the reader to visualize my topic?

• Are my sentences in a logical order?

• Does each paragraph (except for the first) begin with an effective transition?

• Are there other details that I can add as additional body paragraphs to create a fuller or more complete description?

• Are some of my sentences weak or confusing? Should they be removed because they do not relate to the topic?

• Do my body paragraphs appear in the best possible order? Could I place them in a different order that is more logical or effective?

• Is each sentence constructed as well as it should be? *Read each sentence in each paragraph as if it were the only sentence on the page. This helps you to catch sentence*

fragments, run-on sentences, misspellings, and grammatical errors.

- Does my concluding paragraph sum up my main impression of the person, place, object, or event?

Practice   Use the Evaluation Form on the page following this lesson to evaluate the descriptive essay that you wrote for Lesson 26. Read your descriptive essay carefully as you check for the items listed on the Evaluation Form. Write YES or NO in the blank next to each question.

When you are finished, you will either be confident that you have a strong descriptive essay, or you will know where it needs to be improved.

If you answered NO to one or more of the questions on the Evaluation Form, rewrite to improve those areas.

When you can answer YES to every question on the Evaluation Form, you will have completed this assignment.

92

Descriptive Essay Evaluation Form

Topic: _____

_____ Is my introductory sentence interesting? *If it is not interesting to you, it certainly will not be interesting to the reader.*

_____ Does the thesis statement focus on a single person, place, object, or event?

_____ Does the thesis statement give my main impression of that person, place, object, or event?

_____ Does each body paragraph have a clear topic sentence that states the subject of the paragraph? *Read each topic sentence without the rest of the paragraph to see if it can stand alone as a strong idea.*

_____ Do the details all contribute to the reader's ability to visualize or mentally experience my topic?

_____ Within each paragraph, are my sentences in a logical order?

_____ Does each paragraph (except for the first paragraph) begin with an effective transition?

_____ Have I used enough modifiers, comparisons, and sensory expressions to enable the reader to visualize my topic?

_____ Are all of my sentences strong and clear? Do they all directly relate to the topic?

_____ Do my body paragraphs appear in the best possible order? Is their order logical and effective?

_____ Is each sentence structured as well as it could be? *Read each sentence in each paragraph as if it were the only sentence on the page. This helps you to catch sentence fragments and run-on sentences.*

_____ Does my concluding paragraph sum up my main impression of my topic?

93

LESSON 28

Writing a Chapter Summary

A summary is a brief retelling of the main idea(s) in something that one has read. In a summary, the writer omits details and condenses a long passage—a whole story, chapter, or book—to its main idea(s). Therefore, the summary is much shorter than the original passage.

In this lesson, we shall practice writing a one-paragraph summary of a chapter in a novel.

Chapter Summary If you were reading a novel to a friend, and if your friend fell asleep during one of the chapters, he or she might miss a great deal of the action or story line. Your brief *summary* of that missing chapter could help your friend to proceed quickly to the next chapter without confusion and without rereading the entire chapter.

Example Below is a summary of the first chapter of *Beezus and Ramona* by Beverly Cleary. Notice that we use the present tense of verbs.

> Beatrice Quimby, also known as Beezus, has a big problem—her little sister Ramona. One day, to get Ramona to stop riding her tricycles in circles while blowing a mouth organ, Beezus agrees to read Ramona her favorite book—*The Littlest Steam Shovel.* One reading is not enough, for Ramona wants to hear the book again. Out of frustration, Beezus takes Ramona to the library for another book. Ramona chooses *Big Steve the Steam Shovel.* Unfortunately, the book is ruined, for Ramona writes on every page. Embarrassed, Beezus returns to the library with Ramona to pay for the book. Ramona thinks that the book is now hers, but fortunately, Ramona does not succeed in making the book her own.
>
> Summary by Fifi Joyland

Practice In a single paragraph, summarize one chapter of a novel that you are reading or have read in the past (or a novel from the list below). Your summary should include major characters and provide a sense of what happens in the chapter. Remember to use the present tense of verbs.

Suggested novels for this exercise:

The Cricket of Time Square, by George Selden

The Great Brain, by John D. Fitzgerald

James and the Giant Peach, by Roald Dahl

Jumanji, by Chris Van Allsburg

Sadako and the Thousand Paper Cranes, by Eleanor Coerr

The Snow Goose, by Paul Gallico

The Black Stallion, by Walter Farley

M.C. Higgins, the Great, by Virginia Hamilton

LESSON 29

Preparing to Write an Imaginative Story

We have practiced writing vivid descriptions of people, places, objects, or events using details, modifiers, comparisons, and sensory expressions. We have also written a personal narrative with dialogue, logical sentence order, and effective transitions. In this lesson, we shall use all the writing skills we have learned so far in order to create our own imaginative story.

An imaginative story is fiction; it is not a true story although it may be based on something that really happened.

Conflict, characters, setting, and plot are all parts of the imaginative story. In preparing to write our story, we shall gather information concerning each of these parts.

Conflict A short story must have a problem or situation in which struggle occurs. A character may be in conflict with another character, with the forces of nature, with the rules of society, or even with his or her own self, as an internal conflict brought about by pangs of conscience or feelings of ambivalence.

For example, notice the possible conflicts related to the two situations below.

SITUATION 1: Mae does not like brussel sprouts and wants to avoid eating them.

Conflict: A friend serves Mae brussel sprouts.

Conflict: It is impolite not to eat what one is served.

Conflict: Brussel sprouts make Mae gag.

SITUATION 2: Evan has forgotten to bring his homework to school.

Conflict: Evan's teacher might think that he is irresponsible.

Conflict: Evan might receive a low grade for his missing homework.

Conflict: Even might need to miss recess to complete his homework.

96

To find a situation and conflict for your own imaginative story, you might talk to friends or family members, watch the news, read the newspaper, or observe what is happening in the lives of people around you.

In preparation for story-writing, spend several minutes brainstorming with the help of a friend, teacher, or family member to gather ideas of situations and conflicts. Write down all the situations and possible resulting conflicts that come to mind. Then, choose the one conflict that most interests you for your imaginative story.

Tone   Your attitude toward the conflict will create the **tone** of your story. The details and language that you use might evoke joy, fear, amusement, grief, or some other emotion. For example, you will want your story to make the reader laugh if you feel that the situation facing the characters is funny. On the other hand, if you feel that the situation is serious and worrisome, you will try to increase the reader's anxiety.

After choosing your conflict, plan how you will establish the tone of your story by answering the following questions:

1. What is my attitude toward the conflict and the characters involved in it?

2. What details can I use to create this mood, or evoke these emotions, in the reader?

Point of View   You may tell your story from either the first-person or third-person point of view.

In the first-person point of view, the story is narrated, using the pronoun *I*, by one person who either participates in or witnesses the conflict. Only the narrator's thoughts are expressed, as in the example below.

> *Jasmin shared that she loved to read, but she did not tell me the titles of her favorite books.*

In the third-person, or omniscient, point of view, the story is narrated by someone outside the story, someone who knows everything—each character's thoughts and actions. This allows the writer to reveal what any character thinks or does, as in the example below.

97

Jasmin loves to read, especially animal stories and mysteries.

Before you begin writing your imaginative story, you must choose an appropriate point of view from which to tell about the conflict.

Characters To create a captivating story, you must develop interesting and believable characters. Engaged in a struggle, the main character, or *protagonist*, might be opposed by another character, an *antagonist*. There may be other characters as well.

As you develop your characters, attempt to keep them consistent in their behavior and show logical reasons for any change in their behavior. For example, if an ordinarily greedy character suddenly acts generously, you must explain why.

Invent your characters by noting their physical appearances, actions, and personality traits.

Dialogue Dialogue is the spoken words of characters. A character's words can reveal things about the character's personality, background, thoughts, and attitudes. You can use dialogue to develop your characters and make your story more interesting.

Spend a few minutes brainstorming in order to gather ideas about your main characters. Give each one a name, some physical attributes, and a distinctive personality.

Setting The setting is the time and place of the action. Vivid, specific details help to describe the setting of a story. You must consider both location and time. Does your story take place indoors, in a specific room, or outdoors, on a mountain, beach, or prairie? Or, does it take place on an airplane, boat, or train? Do the events occur in the morning, afternoon, or evening? Does the story happen in the past, present, or future?

Decide where and when your story will take place and jot down a few details that you can use later to describe your setting.

98

Plot The plot is the action of your story. Once you have chosen a conflict, one or more characters, and the setting of your story, you are ready to develop the action using this story plan:

BEGINNING OF STORY

Present your characters.

Establish the setting and tone.

Introduce the conflict.

MIDDLE OF STORY

List a series of actions that build to a climax.

END OF STORY

Resolve the conflict, or show why it cannot be resolved.

Use the plan above to make notes, which you can expand later into a full and imaginative story.

Practice Follow the instructions in this lesson for brainstorming, choosing a conflict, deciding on the tone and point of view, inventing characters, describing the setting, and planning the plot of your imaginative story. On a separate piece of paper, answer the following questions:

1. Who are your characters? Give a brief description of each.

2. What is the setting? Give the time and place.

3. Describe the tone: the emotions the reader will experience.

4. What is the conflict?

5. Briefly list some actions that will build to a climax.

6. How will you resolve the conflict?

Keep your answers to these questions in your three-ring binder. In the next lesson, you will use this information as you write your imaginative story.

99

LESSON 30

Writing an Imaginative Story

In Lesson 29, you prepared to write your imaginative story. By brainstorming, you gathered ideas and details. You chose a conflict, you decided on the tone and point of view, you invented characters, you described your setting, and you roughly planned the plot. Now, you are ready to write the imaginative story.

Keep this plan in front of you as you write:

> BEGINNING OF STORY
>
> Present your characters.
>
> Establish the setting and tone.
>
> Introduce the conflict.
>
> MIDDLE OF STORY
>
> List a series of actions that build to a climax.
>
> END OF STORY
>
> Resolve the conflict, or show why it cannot be resolved.

Practice Using your notes from Lesson 29 and the plan above, follow the steps below to write your story.

1. Write an introductory sentence ("hook") that will grab the reader's attention.

2. At the beginning of the story, in whatever order you think is best, establish the setting and tone, present your characters, and introduce the conflict.

3. Add dialogue in order to reveal more about your characters' personalities, thoughts, and motivations.

4. Keep the point of view consistent throughout the story.

5. Write a series of actions that build to a climax.

6. Resolve the conflict at the end of your story, or show why it cannot be resolved.

100

LESSON 31

Evaluating the Imaginative Story

Because *writing is a process,* and all of our writing is "work in progress," we constantly make changes to improve our work. This is especially true when writing an imaginative story. As you create your story, you may see opportunities for revisiting previous parts of your story in order to add more or different traits to a character to explain his or her actions.

Evaluating Your Writing

In Lesson 30, you completed your imaginative story. Now that some time has passed, you are ready to evaluate it using the following guidelines.

Ask yourself these questions:

- Does my introductory sentence ("hook") capture the reader's attention?

- Does the beginning of the story establish the tone and suggest the conflict?

- Are the characters believable and interesting?

- Have I revealed the characters' personalities and motivations through dialogue and action as well as description?

- Are my characters consistent in their behavior? Have I adequately explained any changes from their normal behavior?

- Are there other details, modifiers, comparisons, or sensory expressions that I could add to help the reader to visualize the setting?

- Do the actions flow logically from one to another?

- Do the actions build suspense?

- Does the dialogue sound natural?

- Does the point of view remain constant throughout the story?

- Are some of my sentences weak or confusing? Should any be removed because they do not relate to the story?

101

- Do my sentences appear in the best possible order? Could I place them in a different order that is more logical or effective?

- Is each sentence constructed as well as it should be? *Read each sentence in each paragraph as if it were the only sentence on the page. This helps you to catch sentence fragments, run-on sentences, misspellings, and grammatical errors.*

- Is the end of the story believable and satisfying? Has the conflict been resolved, or have I shown that it cannot be resolved?

Practice   Use the Evaluation Form on the page following this lesson to evaluate the imaginative story that you wrote for Lesson 26. Read your story carefully as you check for the items listed on the Evaluation Form. Write YES or NO in the blank next to each question.

When you are finished, you will either be confident that you have a strong imaginative story, or you will know where it needs to be improved.

If you answered NO to one or more of the questions on the Evaluation Form, rewrite to improve those areas.

When you can answer YES to every question on the Evaluation Form, you will have completed this assignment.

102

Imaginative Story Evaluation Form

Title: _____

_____ Does my introductory sentence ("hook") capture the reader's attention?

_____ Does the beginning of the story establish the tone and suggest the conflict?

_____ Are the characters believable and interesting?

_____ Have I revealed the characters' personalities and motivations through dialogue and action as well as description?

_____ Are my characters consistent in their behavior? Have I adequately explained any change from their normal behavior?

_____ Have I included sufficient details, modifiers, comparisons, and sensory expressions to enable the reader to visualize the setting?

_____ Do the actions flow logically from one to another?

_____ Do the actions build suspense?

_____ Does the dialogue sound natural?

_____ Does the point of view remain consistent throughout the story?

_____ Is each sentence strong and clear? Does each sentence relate to the story?

_____ Is each sentence structured as well as it could be? *Read each sentence in each paragraph as if it were the only sentence on the page. This helps you to catch sentence fragments and run-on sentences.*

_____ Is the end of the story believable and satisfying? Has the conflict been resolved, or have I shown that the conflict cannot be resolved?

103

LESSON 32

Writing about Literature

We read books and magazines for pleasure; however, there are times when we are expected to think and write about what we read.

In this lesson, we will examine the characters in a fictional story, *M. C. Higgins, the Great.*

Read the following excerpt from Chapter 1 of *M. C. Higgins, the Great.* This book is published by Simon and Schuster (New York, 1993) and written by Virginia M. Hamilton.

> Mayo Cornelius Higgins raised his arms high to the sky and spread them wide. He glanced furtively around. It was all right. There was no one to see him greeting the coming sunrise. But the motion of his arms caused a flutter of lettuce leaves he had bound to his wrists with rubber bands. Like bracelets of green feathers, the leaves commenced to wave.

> M. C., as he was called, felt warm, moist air surround him. Humidity trapped in the hills clung to the mountainside as the night passed on. In seconds, his skin grew clammy. But he paid no attention to the oppressive heat with its odors of summer growth and decay. For he was staring out over a grand sweep of hill, whose rolling outlines grew clearer by the minute. As he stood on the gallery of his home, the outcropping on which he lived on the mountainside seemed to fade out from under him.

> I'm standing in mid-air, he thought.

> He saw dim light touch clouds clustered behind the eastern hills.

> Bounce the sun beside me if I want.

> All others in his family were still asleep in the house. To be by himself in the perfect quiet was reason enough for him to wake up way early. Alone for half an hour, he could believe he had been chosen to remain forever suspended, facing the hills. He could pretend there was nothing terrible behind him, above his head. Arms outstretched, picture-framed by pine uprights supporting the gallery roof, he was M. C. Higgins, higher than everything.

104

Practice Referring to the excerpt above, answer the following questions, which examine the character's appreciation of the stillness and beauty of sunrise. You may work alone, with your teacher, or with other students. Remember to use the present tense of verbs.

1. In the passage, what actions show the character's appreciation for the sunrise?

2. Why does M. C. Higgins rise early?

3. Give an example of M. C. Higgins's vivid imagination.

4. Describe the weather.

5. How does M. C. Higgins describe the sun?

6. In the second paragraph, a weather condition is personified. What is personified? How is this weather condition described?

7. Would you call M. C. Higgins eccentric? Why or why not?

*After answering the questions above, compare your answers to the "example answers" on the last few pages of your Writing Packet.

105

LESSON 33

Writing about an Informational Text

Sometimes, we read books and magazines to learn something new or to learn more about a subject. There are times when we are expected to analyze what we read and then write about it.

In this lesson, we shall read for information, with a critical eye, searching for the author's opinions among the facts.

Carefully read the following non-fictional excerpt from "Marsupial Mania." [Montgomery, Sy. *Quest for the Tree Kangaroo: An Expedition to the Cloud Forest of New Guinea.* Orland: Houghton Mifflin, 2006.]

Stuart Little, the small mouse with big parents, had nothing on baby marsupials. Marsupials ("Mar-SOUP-ee-ulz") are special kinds of mammals. Even the biggest ones give birth to babies that are incredibly small. A two-hundred-pound, six-foot, mother kangaroo, for instance, gives birth to a baby as small as a lima bean. That's what makes marsupials marsupials. Their babies are born so tiny that in order to survive they must live in a pouch on the mother's tummy. The pouch is called a marsupium. (Don't you wish you had one?)

A baby marsupial lives hidden in the mother's moist pouch for months. There it sucks milk from a nipple like other baby mammals. One day it's big enough to poke its head out to see the world. The European explorers who saw kangaroos for the first time in Australia reported they had discovered a two-headed animal—with one head on the neck and another in the belly.

North America has only one marsupial. You may have seen it: The Virginia opossum actually lives in most of the United States, not just Virginia. South America also has marsupials. But most marsupials live in or near Australia. They include the koala (which is *not* a bear), two species of wombat, the toothy black Tasmania devil, four species of black and white spotted "native cats" (though they're not cats at all), and many others.

The most famous marsupials, however, are the kangaroos. All kangaroos hop—some of them six feet high and faster than forty miles an hour. More than

fifty different species of kangaroo hop around on the ground—from the big red kangaroo to the musky rat kangaroo.

<u>Practice</u> After reading the excerpt above, answer the following questions. You may work alone, with your teacher, or with other students.

1. What part of this excerpt is fictional?

2. Where does the author express her opinion?

3. What is a *marsupial*?

4. Why did European explorers think that they had found a two-headed animal?

5. Montgomery writes: "Stuart Little, the small mouse with big parents, had nothing on baby marsupials." Is this a fact, or is it Montgomery's opinion?

*When you have completed the practice questions above, compare your answers to the "example answers" on the last few pages of this Writing Packet.

107

LESSON 34

Preparing to Write a Research Paper: The Working Bibliography

A research paper is a type of expository writing based on information gathered from a variety of reliable sources. In the future, you may be asked to write a research paper for an English, history, science, art, or music class. Knowing the procedure for writing a good research paper will help you to become a successful high school and college student.

In this lesson, we shall learn how to prepare for writing a research paper on an assigned subject. To practice the procedure, you may choose one of the following subjects:

1. The Earthworm, a Gardener's Friend

2. How Electricity Was Discovered

3. Eli Whitney's Contribution to the Cultivation of Cotton

4. The Sun: How it Helps and Harms People

5. A subject suggested by your teacher

Tone The research paper requires a serious tone. The writing should be formal and impersonal. Therefore, we do not use first person pronouns, such as *I, me,* or *my*.

Gathering Sources of Information The first step in researching your subject is to compile a **working bibliography,** a collection of possible sources of information. Consider the following possibilities for your research:

- library research aids, such as the card catalog, *Readers' Guide*, and reference works

- Internet

- government publications

- personal interviews of correspondence

- museums

- scholarly journals

108

Evaluating Sources of Information

Not all sources are reliable or useful. We must evaluate each source for its usefulness. Asking the following questions will help us to evaluate each source:

1. *Is the information current?* A description of cell phones in the 1980s would not apply to the cell phone of the twenty-first century. Therefore, it would not be an appropriate source for a paper on today's economy, except for drawing comparisons with the past.

2. *Is the source objective and impartial?* A list, created by a drug company, of the human body's vitamin requirements might not be reliable, for a drug company hopes to sell many vitamins. The author is trying to sell you something.

3. *For what audience was the source intended?* Material written for young children might be over-simplified, and material written for specialists might be too technical.

Preparing Bibliography Cards

After gathering sources, evaluating each one for its usefulness, and choosing only those that are appropriate, we are ready to compile a working bibliography, the list of sources from which we will glean information for our research paper.

Using three-by-five inch index cards, we record each source on a separate card. We include all the information listed below, for we will need it to prepare our final Bibliography when our paper is completed.

BOOKS

1. Author's (or editor's) full name, last name first. Indicate editor by placing *ed.* after the name. If the book has more than one author, only the first author is written last name first. Others are written first name first.

2. Title and subtitle underlined

3. City of publication

4. Publisher's name

5. Most recent copyright year.

109

MAGAZINE, NEWSPAPER, JOURNAL, AND ENCYCLOPEDIA ARTICLES

1. Author's (or editor's) full name, last name first. Indicate editor by placing <u>ed</u>. after the name. If the article has more than one author, only the first author is written last name first. Others are written first name first.

2. Title of article in quotation marks

3. Name of magazine, newspaper, journal, or encyclopedia underlined

4. Date and page numbers of *magazines*
   Date, edition, section, page numbers of *newspapers*
   Volume, year, page numbers of *journals*
   Edition and year of *encyclopedias*

ELECTRONIC SOURCES

1. Author's (or editor's) full name, last name first. Indicate editor by placing <u>ed</u>. after the name. If the article has more than one author, only the first author is written last name first. Others are written first name first.

2. Title of article in quotation marks

3. Books, magazines, newspapers, journals, encyclopedias, or Web sites underlined

4. Date and page numbers of magazines.

   Date, edition, section, page numbers of newspapers.

   Volume, year, page numbers of journals

   Edition and year of encyclopedia.

   City of publication, publisher's name, and most recent copyright year of books.

5. The date that you accessed the source

6. The URL in angle brackets

110

We assign each bibliography card a "source number" and write it in the upper left corner. Later, we will use this number to identify the sources of our notes. Below are some sample bibliography cards.

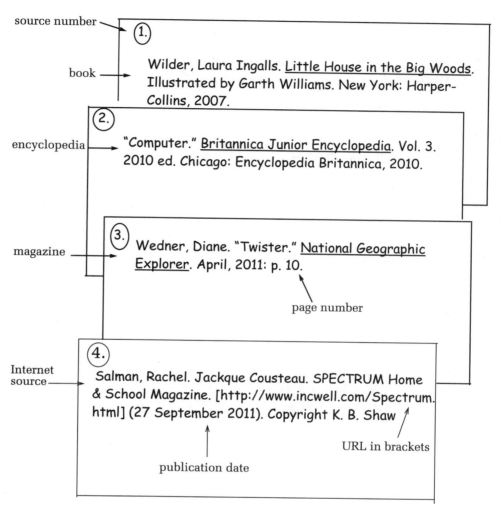

source number

①.

book → Wilder, Laura Ingalls. <u>Little House in the Big Woods</u>. Illustrated by Garth Williams. New York: Harper-Collins, 2007.

②.

encyclopedia → "Computer." <u>Britannica Junior Encyclopedia</u>. Vol. 3. 2010 ed. Chicago: Encyclopedia Britannica, 2010.

③.

magazine → Wedner, Diane. "Twister." <u>National Geographic Explorer</u>. April, 2011: p. 10.

page number

④.

Internet source → Salman, Rachel. Jackque Cousteau. SPECTRUM Home & School Magazine. [http://www.incwell.com/Spectrum.html] (27 September 2011). Copyright K. B. Shaw

URL in brackets

publication date

Practice After you have chosen a subject from the list of suggestions for your research paper, follow the instructions in this lesson for gathering and evaluating sources and for preparing bibliography cards. Locate at least four appropriate sources and prepare a bibliography card for each one. Remember to assign each card a source number and write it in the upper left corner.

111

LESSON 35

Preparing to Write a Research Paper: Notes, Thesis, Outline

In the last lesson, you chose a subject for a research paper and created a working bibliography. This listed at least four sources of information that you will use for your paper. In this lesson, you will take notes from these sources, organize your notes, create a thesis statement, and develop an outline for your paper.

Taking Notes It is helpful to use four-by-six inch index cards for taking notes. As you read through your sources, write down information that applies to your subject. Write most of your notes in your own words. You may summarize the author's main ideas, or you may record specific facts or details in your own words. If you quote the author, you must enclose the author's exact words in quotation marks.

Whenever you take notes from a source, you must credit that source whether you quote an author or use your own words. Do not *plagiarize*, or use another person's words or ideas, without acknowledging the source.

In the upper right corner of your note card, you will enter the source number from your working bibliography.

At the end of each note, write the page or pages on which you found the information.

Below is a sample note card.

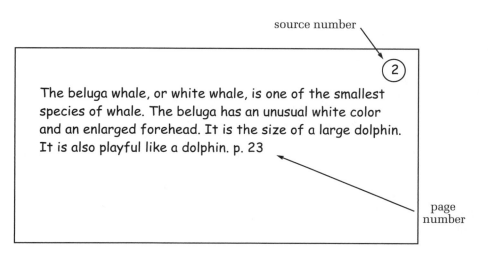

source number

The beluga whale, or white whale, is one of the smallest species of whale. The beluga has an unusual white color and an enlarged forehead. It is the size of a large dolphin. It is also playful like a dolphin. p. 23

page number

112

Organizing Your Information After you have taken notes on all your sources and gathered sufficient information for your research paper, take some time to organize your note cards and arrange them in a logical order.

Thesis Statement Now, look over your organized notes and write a thesis statement that clearly explains the main idea of your research paper.

Outline In Lesson 17, you learned to develop an outline. Use your organized note cards to help you create an informal topic outline for your research paper. This outline will guide you as you begin to write the first draft of your paper in the next lesson.

Practice Follow the instructions in this lesson for taking notes from your sources. Then, organize your notes, write a thesis statement, and develop an outline for your research paper.

113

LESSON 36

Writing the Research Paper

In the last lesson, you took notes from your sources, organized your notes, wrote a thesis statement, and created an outline for your research paper.

Writing the First Draft

With your outline, your thesis statement, your notes, and your bibliography cards in front of you, you are ready to begin writing the first draft of your research paper. A first draft is a rough copy that is for your use only. It is meant to be revised again and again until you are satisfied with it.

As you write, keep in mind your thesis statement, your purpose, and the need for a formal tone. Use the information on your note cards to support your thesis and to fill in the details as you follow your outline for organization.

Create an opening paragraph that captures the reader's attention. Consider beginning with an interesting statement, an anecdote, or an example. Make certain that your opening paragraph includes your thesis statement.

Use the main points in your outline to create topic sentences for your body paragraphs. Then, expand these topic sentences into paragraphs, making sure that all of your information relates to your thesis statement.

Pay special attention to transitions as you begin each new paragraph.

Your concluding paragraph will summarize and reinforce the ideas set forth in the rest of your research paper.

Documentation of Sources

Writing the first draft of a research paper involves bringing together information from your different sources, which you must acknowledge property. We call this **documentation of sources.**

As you write, you must credit your sources for both ideas and quotations. There are various methods of documenting sources for research papers. In this book, we shall practice a method called *parenthetical citations.* This form identifies sources in parentheses that are placed as close as possible to the ideas or quotations that we cite.

114

Inside the parentheses, we place a reference to the source on our bibliography card. Usually, the reference inside the parentheses consists only of an author's last name and page number from which the material was taken.

For example, (Wilder 25) would appear right after an idea taken from page twenty-five in Laura Ingalls Wilder's book.

When no author and only a title is given for a source, we place a shortened form of the title and the page number or numbers in the parentheses: ("The Pet Goat" 46-47).

In the example below, notice that the end punctuation for a sentence containing borrowed material is placed *after* the parenthetical citation.

> Juan Ponce de Leon, a Spanish conquistador, was an explorer who "desired riches" (Calkins 1).

punctuation mark

The highly respected Modern Language Association (MLA) gives us many more detailed guidelines for parenthetical citations. However, in this lesson, we shall follow the simplified instructions above.

The Bibliography The **bibliography,** the list of the sources that you used as you wrote your paper, comes at the end of the research paper.

Follow these steps to create your bibliography:

1. Alphabetize your bibliography cards according to the last names of the authors or the first important word in a title if there is no author.

2. Copy the information from all of your alphabetized bibliography cards under the title "Bibliography" or "Works Cited."

3. Indent all lines after the first line of each entry and punctuate as shown in the example below.

Bibliography

Calkins, Virginia. "The Explorers: Spanish Beginnings in North America." Cobblestone Magazine, April, 1989: 1-2.

Sendak, Maurice. Where the Wildthings Are. New York: Harper Collins Publishers, 1988.

115

In higher grades, you will learn to follow more detailed guidelines for bibliographic entries. However, in this lesson, you may follow the simplified instructions above unless your teacher asks you to do otherwise.

Practice   Follow the procedure given in this lesson for writing the first draft of your research paper and for creating your bibliography, or list of works cited.

LESSON 37

Evaluating the Research Paper

The knowledge that *writing is a process* guides our thinking throughout the construction of our research paper. From the first steps in choosing our subject, to gathering information and organizing our thoughts, to creating body paragraphs, to adding transitions, we constantly make changes to improve our work.

Evaluating Your Writing

In the last lesson, you completed the first draft of your research paper. Now that some time has passed, you are ready to evaluate it using the following guidelines.

Ask yourself these questions:

- Are my sources reliable, objective, and current?

- Is my introductory sentence interesting? *If it is not interesting to you, it certainly will not be interesting to the reader.*

- Does my thesis clearly state the purpose of my paper?

- Does the beginning of the research paper clearly establish a formal, serious tone?

- Does each body paragraph have a clear topic sentence that states the subject of the paragraph? *Read each topic sentence without the rest of the paragraph to see if it can stand alone as a strong idea.*

- Does each paragraph include specific details and examples from my research?

- Have I correctly documented each piece of borrowed information?

- Are my sentences in a logical order?

- Does each paragraph (except for the first) begin with an effective transition?

- Are there other details that I can add as additional body paragraphs to create a fuller or more complete paper?

- Are some of my sentences weak or confusing? Should they be removed because they do not relate to my thesis?

- Do my body paragraphs appear in the best possible order? Could I place them in a different order that is more logical or effective?

- Is each sentence constructed as well as it should be? *Read each sentence in each paragraph as if it were the only sentence on the page. This helps you to catch sentence fragments, run-on sentences, misspellings, and grammatical errors.*

- Does my ending paragraph obviously conclude my presentation? Does it reinforce my thesis statement?

Practice   Use the Evaluation Form on the page following this lesson to evaluate the research paper you wrote for Lesson 16. Read your research paper carefully as you check for the items listed on the Evaluation Form. Write YES or NO in the blank next to each question.

When you are finished, you will either be confident that you have a strong research paper, or you will know where it needs to be improved.

If you answered NO to one or more of the questions on the Evaluation Form, rewrite to improve those areas.

When you can answer YES to every question on the Evaluation Form, you will have completed this assignment.

118

Research Paper Evaluation Form

Subject: _____

_____ Is my introductory sentence interesting? *If it is not interesting to you, it certainly will not be interesting to the reader.*

_____ Does the beginning of the research paper clearly establish a formal, serious tone?

_____ Does the thesis clearly state the purpose of the paper?

_____ Does each body paragraph have a clear topic sentence that tells the subject of the paragraph? *Read each topic sentence without the rest of the paragraph to see if it can stand alone as a strong idea.*

_____ Do the details all contribute to the reader's understanding of the thesis?

_____ Within each paragraph, are my sentences in a logical or practical order?

_____ Does each paragraph (except for the first paragraph) begin with an effective transition?

_____ Is each piece of borrowed material given proper credit?

_____ Are all of my sentences strong and clear? Do they all directly relate to the thesis?

_____ Do my body paragraphs appear in the best possible order? Is their order logical and effective?

_____ Is each sentence structured as well as it could be? *Read each sentence in each paragraph as if it were the only sentence on the page. This helps you to catch sentence fragments, run-on sentences, and other errors.*

_____ Does my concluding paragraph summarize my research and reinforce my thesis statement?

_____ Are my sources reliable, objective, and current?

119

LESSON 38

Idioms and Proverbs

Idioms An **idiom** is a phrase or expression whose meaning cannot be understood from the dictionary meanings of the words in it. For example, "Hold your tongue" is an English idiom meaning "be quiet" or "keep still."

Practice Working by yourself or with others, write the meaning of each English idiom below.

1. A blessing in disguise

   _____

2. A chip on your shoulder

   _____

3. A doubting Thomas

   _____

4. A house divided against itself cannot stand

   _____

5. A piece of cake

   _____

6. A slap on the wrist

   _____

Can you think of other English idioms? List as many as you can and write their meanings.

120

Proverbs   A **proverb,** or adage, is a short, wise saying used for a long time by many people. "Don't put the cart before the horse" is a proverb meaning "do not reverse the normal order of things."

Practice   Working by yourself or with others, write the meanings of the proverbs below.

1. A chain is only as strong as its weakest link.

   _____

2. A dog is man's best friend.

   _____

3. A fool and his money are soon parted.

   _____

4. A good man is hard to find.

   _____

5. A person is known by the company that he keeps.

   _____

6. A poor workman always blames his tools.

   _____

When you have finished this lesson, compare your answers to those at the end of this Writing Packet.

Can you think of other proverbs? List as many as you can and write their meanings.

Appendix

Example Outline for Lesson 18

I. Fresh Produce
   A. Fruits
      1. Plums
      2. Watermelons
      3. Cherries
      4. Apples
      5. Grapes
   B. Vegetables
      1. Corn
      2. Squash
      3. Peas
      4. Green beans

Answers for Lesson 25

a. a large, thick English book

b. an old aluminum roasting pan

c. an ugly grey beach towel

Example Answers for Lesson 32

1. Mayo Cornelius Higgins raises his arms and opens them wide to welcome the sun. He speaks about the beauty of nature around him in artistic terms. M. C. Higgins describes himself as "framed" by pine trees and standing in mid-air.

2. M. C. Higgins rises early to view the sunrise and to be by himself. The author suggests that he is part of a busy, noisy family and wants to be alone to appreciate the beauty of his surroundings.

3. As mentioned in the answer to the first question, M. C. Higgins's vivid imagination is expressed in the way that he describes himself as standing in the middle of a picture in the gallery of nature.

4. The weather is hot and damp. The humidity is oppressive.

5. M. C. Higgins describes the sun as "touch[ing] the clouds and bounc[ing] beside him."

6. "Humidity … clung to the mountainside."

7. M. C. Higgins might have been eccentric because he had lettuce leaves attached to the sleeves of his shirt.

Example Answers for Lesson 33

1. Stuart Little and his parents are fictional.

2. The author asks the readers if they wish that they had a pouch. The author claims that kangaroos are the most famous marsupials, but he does not support this statement with facts.

3. A marsupial is a special kind of mammal that bears babies that are so small that they must live in the mother's pouch.

4. European explorers believed this because they saw baby marsupials pop their heads out of the mothers' pouches. These explorers thought that marsupials had a head on their necks and a head on their bellies.

5. This statement is an example of an opinion.

Example Answers for Lesson 38

Idioms

1. A blessing in disguise: a good thing that you do not realize at first.

2. A chip on your shoulder: being angry about something that happened in the past.

3. A doubting Thomas: someone who will not easily believe something unless there is lots of evidence.

4. A house divided against itself cannot stand: unity means strength; dissension means weakness.

5. A piece of cake: a task that can be done easily.

6. A slap on the wrist: to receive a slight punishment.

Proverbs

1. A chain is only as strong as its weakest link: If the weakest person fails, the whole project fails. A team is only as strong as its weakest player.

2. A dog is man's best friend: A dog is more faithful than most friends.

3. A fool and his money are soon parted: A fool either wastes his money or is tricked out of it.

4. A good man is hard to find: Good spouses, good friends, good workers, and good people are hard to find.

5. A person is known by the company that he keeps: People who are alike hang around each other.

6. A poor workman always blames his tools: This is a person who blames other things or other people for his or her mistakes.